HEREFORD
WORCEST

RRID
R

R.MONNOW

MONMOUTH

REDDING'S
INCLOSURE

RAGLAN

TRELLECK

CLEDDON BOG

G L O U C E S T E R S H I R E

DEVAUDEN

TINTERN

USK

R. WYE

R. USK

WENTWOOD
RES.

CHEPSTOW

CALDICOT

UNDY

SUDBROOK

REDWICK

MOUTH OF THE SEVERN

FF

FORESTRY/WOODLAND

LAND ABOVE 800 FT.
(250 METRES)

D. F. Tansley 1977

THE BIRDS OF GWENT

Keri Williams　　　　DIPPER

THE
BIRDS
OF
GWENT

Edited and written by

P. N. FERNS   H. W. HAMAR

P. N. HUMPHREYS   F. D. KELSEY

E. T. SARSON   W. A. VENABLES

I. R. WALKER

With additional material by

K. JONES   W. G. LEWIS   B. M. MORGAN   P. F. J. PLAYFORD

GWENT
ORNITHOLOGICAL
SOCIETY
1977

ISBN 0 9505760 0 X

Printed in Great Britain by
Hughes & Son Ltd.,
The Griffin Press,
Pontypool, Gwent.

CONTENTS

LIST OF PLATES

facing page

FOREWORD

Having had the good fortune to be born in Gwent (or Monmouth-shire, as it then was) and now to be living in the county once more, it gives me particular pleasure to commend this book.

Gwent has for long been an under-recorded county, and under-valued by most people not fortunate enough to live in it. However, the recent publication of *The Atlas of Breeding Birds of Britain and Ireland* must have caused many general readers to want to know more about the ' real-life stories ' lying behind those necessarily cryptic symbols. For them, *The Birds of Gwent* is an introduction to the history of bird study in the county, to the particular sites which they may wish to visit and the birds they may hope to see, with a word, too, about our hopes and fears for the future.

As for those of us who are more personally involved in the birds of our home county, this book cannot fail to be an absorbing source for reference and comparison, as year by year we observe those subtle changes which can be so significant to the future of wildlife populations.

I warmly recommend *The Birds of Gwent* to all inhabitants of the county, and all who share our interest in this very lovely and varied part of Wales.

DILYS BREESE
Itton, Gwent, April 1977.

INTRODUCTION

THE small western county, known for centuries as Monmouthshire, and now, obscurely, as Gwent, has produced three books on its ornithology in the last forty years. The first, the Birds of Monmouthshire, was published as a reprint of a section of the Cardiff Naturalists' Society's Transactions in 1937. Its authors, the well-known ornithologists G.C.S. Ingram and H. Morrey Salmon, also published accounts of the ornithology of several neighbouring Welsh counties at about the same time and thus formalised a great many manuscript records, museum lists etc., which would otherwise have passed into oblivion. In addition, they made extensive observations of their own and did a great deal of field-work in South Wales at a time when bird-watching was considered to be almost an eccentricity. The Birds of Monmouthshire was revised and up-dated by P. N. Humphreys in 1963 and published by the Newport Museum. Considerable assistance in this was provided by Dr. Bruce Campbell who had lived in the county for a period in the 1940s and had written a Ph.D. thesis on the status of the birds inhabiting the " rural " and " industrial " farmland of South Wales, which included much land in Monmouthshire. During the 1960s ornithology achieved great popularity as a leisure interest and the Gwent Ornithological Society, in its infancy at the beginning of the decade, had a large and growing membership at the end of it. The increased numbers of people recording bird numbers and occurrences meant that the previous books grew rapidly out of date and it was to try and rectify this unsatisfactory state of affairs that the Society appointed a committee to produce a new volume for the county, bringing together not only records of occurrences but results of population surveys, migration studies, special projects and effects of environmental change on our local avifauna.

The Birds of Gwent is therefore a corporate effort, rather than the work of one person. It is possible that this may be apparent to the reader, but it is hoped that the distracting effect will be minimal as the editorial committee has worked very closely together and each section has been examined and constructively criticised by more than one person. Certain parts of the book have been written by members of the Society who have not been members of the committee but who have specialist knowledge and experience, and the maps and photographs have been provided by non-committee members also, so that in a real sense, this book is very much a distillation of the expertise of all the members of the Gwent Ornithological Society.

There has been some criticism in the ornithological press that county " bird books " are anachronistic in these days of national or even international surveys of population trends and statistical calculations of this or that climatic influence, and that a detailed account by a number of people (not necessarily in the ornithological " establishment ") of a small area of one small country can contribute little to the overall sum of human knowledge about birds. We do not see it quite that way. A county ornithology is another way of looking at a county. As such, it is as useful to the reader studying the area as a flora, an economic survey or a geological assessment or any other source of knowledge. We have come to realise that decisions affecting our surroundings can only be taken when ALL the possible factors likely to be influences for good or bad have been assessed; for this purpose a county ornithology offers a guide to the biological quality of each and every habitat in that county. The casual or occasional visitor to Gwent has also been kept in mind. A person who has only a few days or weeks to spend in an area wants to know what sort of birds he is likely to see and where. For that reason a special chapter on the most favoured ornithological sites has been included. This does not mean, of course, that there are no birds elsewhere in the county; in fact Gwent is singularly rich in interesting habitats and can boast many beautiful and secluded corners still little affected by urban sprawl or " agribusiness." There are no sea-cliffs in Gwent, and very little shingle beach; we are also lacking sand-dunes, so that species such as the auks and terns are uncommon visitors. Nor is the county likely to be visited by the ornithologist keen on rarities; the county lies a little off the main migration routes of the east and west coasts and generally there has to be a fairly massive invasion from the continent before Gwent bird-watchers report such species as Nutcrackers and Waxwings. Nevertheless, the records are rich in waders from the Severn estuary, warblers from the extensive woodlands, Ravens and Ring Ouzels from the mountains and ducks and grebes from the reservoirs. The topography of the agricultural part of the county, with a rich sandstone soil and smallish farms with a stock-raising tradition, means that hedgerows, small woodlands and brooks persist, thus ensuring an equally rich variety of bird life.

The earliest known interest in any form of ornithology in the county appears to have been the construction of two duck decoys at Nash and Wilcrick about the middle of the eighteenth century. The Birds of Monmouthshire of 1937 relates that they each covered about an acre and had six pipes, but fell into disuse when the railway was built close to them. The site of one of them at least seems to have survived in the form of an informal lake near the offices of the Spencer Steel Works at Llanwern and still attracts waterfowl in small numbers, especially in the winter. Later, it became fashionable to make collections of stuffed birds and the most notable seems to have been the collection of a Mr. William Conway in the neighbourhood of Pontypool, made during the first half of the 19th century. Some of this came to the National Museum of Wales in the 1880s. Mr. Percy Laybourne, of Newport also made a collection in the last 15 years of the nineteenth century and shot many of the birds in it himself, but he seems to have left few records and the collection eventually went to the Newport Museum.

A collection of eggs, which was recently rediscovered and examined by members of the Gwent Ornithological Society, was made by the late Mr. W. Baker-Gabb, of The Chain, Abergavenny, between 1889 and 1919, and meticulously catalogued together with details of site, clutch size, nest material etc. It is interesting to read of a Corncrake's nest composed of pieces of carpet, among other materials!

These old collections were sometimes supplied by taxidermists without too much regard for the truthfulness of the site record from which the specimen was supposed to have originated. Since it has become known that eminent ornithologists of the time were duped in this respect (see " The Hastings Rarities," British Birds 55, 8, 1962) we have thought it advisable to omit from the records certain birds said to have been collected in the neighbourhood of Pontypool, including Bee-eater, Roller, Crested Tit and a Hoopoe " with a nest and eight eggs," which all seem to have been part of Mr. Conway's collection. The data which the early Museum curators kept appear to have been very sketchy as well; another record, that of a case containing a family of Great Crested Grebes recently on display in the National Museum of Wales and labelled Marshfield, turns out to be no more than a record of the address of the person who supplied them to the Museum! The birds are much more likely to have come from Llangorse Lake, in Powys.

The changes in attitudes to birds can be seen in the absence of recent records of birds " collected " or shot, and only the most perverted now collect eggs (albeit illegally). Instead, the development of binoculars, telescopes and telescopic lenses on cameras make it possible to see and photograph birds which our ancestors could only examine after killing them. Similarly, the advent of bird ringing and netting on a large scale has enabled ornithologists to handle and acquaint themselves with live birds which they may meet again in another year or another place. There is therefore no excuse to take life now. We should be grateful to the old collectors and their victims for the knowledge they brought to an infant science, but we must be glad their habits have died with them.

This is not to say that the birds are not being killed by vandals and hooligans, as they must always have been. Although the bird protection legislation in this country is very comprehensive, it is another matter to enforce it and many instances have come to us over the years of nests being robbed, birds shot and maimed or in some cases, stolen by falconers' touts for sale. Destruction of birds of prey by game-preserving interests also continues, but fortunately not as much as in some other counties. The re-population of the agricultural districts of Gwent by the Buzzard and Raven, at one time reduced to the status of refugees in the mountain zones, shows that gamekeeping is now exercised with more discretion and understanding. Since 1963, when the revised Birds of Monmouthshire was published, there have been some changes in habitat which have affected the areas of most ornithological interest. In particular, Caldicot Moor and Undy Pool, which were regularly flooded in the winter, have been drained, and thus have been lost wonderful areas for migrating waterfowl and waders in the spring. To balance this loss must be put the development of Llandegfedd Reservoir as a winter refuge for very large numbers of duck and Coot and as an example of a water habitat which was formerly lacking in the county. It is pleasant to record the friendly co-operation the Society has had from the Reservoir Authorities ever since the completion of the reservoir. The destruction of the reed beds and marshy ground in the neighbourhood of Newport Docks has been a blow from which there is unlikely to be any compensation, especially as this sort of habitat is now very scarce; but if wisdom prevailed even now a certain amount could be saved. Pollution of rivers and watercourses has been decreasing as manufacturing concerns have been forced to act a little more responsibly with the result that some very grossly polluted rivers, such as the Afon Llwyd, have become tolerably clean, and have been recolonised by Kingfishers, Dippers and Grey Wagtails. The same cannot be said of the Monmouthshire canal from Pontypool to Brecon, which has been greatly overused by pleasure craft leading to some pollution and considerable disturbance in the breeding season.

Changes in distribution due to alteration of climatic conditions, which are thought to be responsible for certain extensions and diminutions of species ranges, are more subtle and become apparent only in the course of many years. The Red-backed Shrike, which seems to have been fairly plentiful in the county in the last century has been seen only very rarely since the Second World War; the Nightingale, once so common that it gave its name to several places (Pant-yr-eos, Risca; Nightingale Row, Cwmbran) is only a sporadic visitor and the Wryneck which was breeding around Abergavenny in Baker-Gabb's time vanished from the scene during the first half of the century, only to turn up again as an almost regular autumn passage migrant during the last decade. The spectacular explosion of the Collared Dove into this country in the 1950s could not have been predicted, nor could the fluctuations in numbers of some summer migrants due to adverse conditions in their wintering areas. It is thus impossible to produce a definitive book and place the birds in " their proper stations " for all time. Change is the one constant feature of life.

We have tried to make this a readable book and have somewhat simplified the format of the text by using only the common English names and scientific binomials without attributions. There is a separate list of Welsh bird-names. In view of the trend towards metrication, which will be well advanced by the time this book appears in print, metric units have been adopted throughout, followed by their imperial equivalents. Since nearly all heights, distances and areas referred to are approximate, both metric and imperial measures have been given only to the accuracy which the context justifies, so that the converted figures may not correspond exactly. The standard abbreviations for units have been used, except that the word hectare(s) has been retained in full, as the standard abbreviation ha. may not be widely familiar. We have also omitted the old practice of attributing records to individual observers, as the list would now be so long as to merit another chapter of the book. Most of the detailed information on records can be found in the two previous county ornithologies and in the annual reports of the Gwent Ornithological Society. Acknowledgements will be found with respect to individual chapters but it would be impertinent to close this introduction without mentioning the debt of gratitude we owe to many members of the Society and the Gwent Trust for Nature Conservation, Dunlop Semtex Ltd., and Parke Davis Ltd., for financial contributions which have made the book possible, to Keri Williams, Clive Landen and Bill Keen for their beautiful photographs, to Betty Morgan and D. Tansley for the maps, to Mrs. E. Worrall for many hours of conscientious typing and to our publishers, The Griffin Press of Pontypool who have all along taken a personal interest in the production of the volume and have been extremely understanding and generous in their terms.

PATRICK HUMPHREYS.

THE GWENT ORNITHOLOGICAL SOCIETY

The Society was founded in 1961 by a group of amateur ornithologists from the Pontypool district who met at the house of Mr. and Mrs. H. W. Hamar to swap notes and talk about their hobby. In 1963 it was decided to formalise the situation and the Pontypool Ornithological Society was born with P. N. Humphreys elected as President, H. J. Vernall as Chairman, H. W. Hamar Secretary and A. V. Allingham Treasurer. The expansion of the Society soon meant that the cosiness of the Hamar family sitting-room had to be abandoned for a more public and spacious venue and the Goytre Village Hall has served as a regular meeting place for most of the life of the Society except for a short period at Panteg. Meetings have been held at other locations in the county on occasion, however.

As the size and distribution of the membership grew it was decided to change the name of the Society to that of the Monmouthshire Ornithological Society and after the re-organisation of local government boundaries to the Gwent Ornithological Society.

The activities of the Society have included the production of an Annual Report giving details of Society affairs and bird records for the previous year; considerable field work with a regular programme of indoor and outdoor meetings and in recent years an Annual Dinner which has enabled members to enjoy a relaxed social evening and to entertain distinguished friends of the Society.

The membership has levelled off in the 1970s to approximately 300, although of course new members are always made welcome. The Society has been fortunate in maintaining a degree of stability and enthusiasm over a considerable period and has many of the first committee members still active in Society affairs; with some, such as H. W. Hamar and P. N. Humphreys still in their original posts as Secretary and President respectively. Another long-serving officer has been Mrs. Queenie Saunders, who succeeded A. V. Allingham as Treasurer in 1967. Past Chairmen have included Mrs. S. H. Robbins, W. G. Lewis and E. T. Sarson. The emminent ornithologists H. Morrey Salmon and Dr. Bruce Campbell have both been Honorary Members for many years and still visit the Society from time to time.

Membership of the Society, which is noted for its friendly and informal atmosphere, is open to any person of whatever age who has a genuine interest in birds, regardless of their degree of knowledge, and although the subscription has had to be altered from time to time it has always been kept low enough to prevent it becoming an obstacle to recruitment. " The Birds of Gwent " is the Society's first major publication.

CHAPTER 1

TOPOGRAPHY

by B. M. MORGAN

IT was on 1st April 1974 with the re-organisation of Local Government that the county lost its cherished name of Monmouthshire and became known as the county of Gwent.

The county was divided up into five districts, the western half comprising Torfaen, Islwyn, Blaenau Gwent and Newport while Monmouth district formed the eastern half. Some land was gained and some lost. On the western boundary parts of the former Rural District of Magor and St. Mellons and parts of Bedwas and Machen Urban Districts and Rhymney Valley Urban District were all lost to the newly created counties of Mid and South Glamorgan. In total 1068 hectares (2639 acres) were lost in the Rhymney Valley area, and 750 hectares (1853 acres) were lost in the Magor and St. Mellons districts. Parts of the former county of Brecknock on the north-west boundary of Monmouthshire were absorbed into the new administrative area, as also was the former County Borough of Newport in the south. Land gained totalled some 590 hectares (1458 acres) at Brynmawr and 2421 hectares (5980 acres) between Brynmawr and Gilwern.

The county boundary in the north-west adjoins the new county of Powys; in the north-east it adjoins the new county of Hereford and Worcester; along the eastern side it adjoins Gloucestershire, while in the west it adjoins the two new counties of Mid and South Glamorgan.

The Bristol Channel forms the southern boundary of the county. The Wye and its tributary, the Monnow, form the eastern and north-eastern boundaries except for a small digression around the town of Monmouth. The north-western boundary is an arbitrary one drawn in erratic fashion in a more or less west to east direction across the high plateau from the source of the Rhymney to the Usk valley near Gilwern. Here it turns northwards and takes in a long narrow extension which includes the greater part of the Vale of Ewyas or Llanthony Valley, before it reaches the eastern boundary at the junction of the Honddu and Monnow rivers.

Physically, the county is sharply divided into three main areas:—

(a) The coastal alluvial levels.

(b) The central area which extends from the south-west to north-east boundaries.

(c) The uplands of the north and north-west.

The coastal levels extend from the western boundary at Peterstone Wentlooge almost to the eastern boundary at the mouth of the Wye.

The main Cardiff to Newport road and the motorway from Newport to Chepstow form a convenient boundary between the coastal and central area. A line drawn from Machen through Pontypool to Abergavenny and continued along the River Monnow to the Hereford and Worcester border separates the central area from the uplands.

The upland area is in two distinct parts. In the north-west there is the highly industrial area which forms what is known as the eastern valleys of the South Wales coalfield. Beyond the Usk valley is a narrow strip, extending northwards into the Black Mountains between Powys and Hereford and Worcester which may be termed the northern area and which is completely rural in character.

The area from Peterstone to the mouth of the Usk is known as the Wentlooge Level. It extends about 3 km (2 miles) inland from the sea wall which runs along the entire foreshore and safeguards the low lying land from flooding at high tide. The altitude above mean sea level is between 4 m (13 ft.) and 6 m (20 ft.) so that practically the whole area is well below the height of most spring tides, the rise and fall of which reaches a maximum of 12 m (39 ft.) at Cardiff and 14.5 m (48 ft.) at Newport.

The area from the mouth of the Usk at Newport, eastwards to the Severn Bridge (opened in 1966) is known as the Caldicot Level and extends 5 km (3 miles) inland. The general character of the Wentlooge and Caldicot Levels is the same, with flat grassland divided into small fields by ditches which connect into larger drainage channels called reens.

Geologically, the central area is of the upper and lower series of Old Red Sandstone with a small area of Silurian shales and this tends to make undulating country. Except for the industrial district between Newport and Pontypool, the whole area is predominantly agricultural. A relatively large area of agricultural land has gradually been developed into the newly built town of Cwmbran which had a population of 45,000 in the year 1974. The building of Cwmbran still continues westwards towards Mynydd Henllys and therefore taking over many more hectares of agricultural land.

The whole of the north-western part of Gwent is industrialised. though between the steep-sided, narrow valleys there are extensive high moorlands. Most of the moorland is above the 450 m (1,500 ft.) contour and there are several regions considerably higher than this, for example, the Blorenge (559 m; 1,833 ft.) in the north-east, Twyn Ceilog (554 m; 1,818 ft.) in the north-west and highest of all, Coity Mountain at 581 m (1,905 ft.).

To the north of the Usk valley lies the northern part of the upland area, covering some 7,800 hectares (30 square miles) in the Black Mountains and geologically of the upper series of Old Red Sandstone. The jointed structure of these rocks, combined with their steep dip, mainly from north to south, produces escarpments of no great height on the north-east faces of the long ridges of the Black Mountains, but only one such ridge lies within the county boundaries. The whole of this area is comparatively high, the greater part being over 300 m (1,000 ft.) and on the county boundary there are six peaks between 600 m (1,955 ft.) and 680 m (2,228 ft.).

The county is fortunate in having artificial reservoirs of considerable area. Wentwood Reservoir, opened in 1904, is situated on the western slopes of Gray Hill in close proximity to the mainly coniferous Wentwood. It lies on the 137 m (450 ft.) contour and covers an area of 16 hectares (39 acres). Excavations for Llandegfedd Reservoir started in April 1961 and in 1964 it was supplying water. It is situated east of Pontypool lying on the 90 m (300 ft.) contour and has an area of 173 hectares (428 acres). This reservoir is fed principally by water pumped from the River Usk but also receives some inflow from the Sor Brook.

In April 1975 the population of Gwent was 439,300 and the total area 137,629 hectares (339,944 acres). Farmland totalled 79,000 hectares (195,132 acres) with rough grazing taking up 6,170 hectares (15,229 acres).

Approximately $13\frac{1}{2}\%$ of Gwent is covered by woodland. There are 5,060 hectares (12,500 acres) in private ownership, while 9,400 hectares (23,200 acres) are owned by the Forestry Commission and Dedicated and Approved woodland totals 1,800 hectares (4,500 acres). Small woods of under 2 hectares (5 acres) and usually deciduous are estimated to comprise just over one-third of the county's total woodland area. 80% of existing woodland blocks of over 2 hectares (5 acres) is under forest management and the majority of these are in Forestry Commission ownership.

Climatic conditions in Gwent vary according to position and altitude. The average annual rainfall is 76 cm to 89 cm (30 to 35 in.) on the coastal levels; 81 cm to 102 cm (32 to 40 in.) in the central and eastern areas, and 178 cm (70 in.) on the Black Mountains north of Tredegar and Ebbw Vale. Naturally, snow is less frequent on the lowland areas than on the higher valley plateaux.

CHAPTER 2

IMPORTANT SITES

by K. Jones and W. A. Venables

DURING 1976 the British Trust for Ornithology completed its " Ornithological Site Register," a project aimed at identification, description and evaluation of all sites of ornithological importance throughout Britain. Each site was visited regularly during all seasons to build an accurate picture of the habitats it contained, the number and variety of birds present, and the use they made of the area.

The criteria for the selection of sites throughout Britain were:

(i) threatened or potentially threatened habitats

(ii) sites with locally or nationally scarce species

(iii) sites with important numbers of birds, whether breeding, feeding, roosting or other

(iv) sites with a good bird community or high diversity

(v) good amenity areas

(vi) important passage sites

The result for Gwent has been the description and registration of a total of 53 sites scattered throughout the county. Almost certainly the most important consequence of this will be that whenever an area of ornithological importance is threatened in the future, detailed data to demonstrate its importance will be available and will be a priceless asset if it should be necessary to make a case for its conservation.

The remainder of this chapter describes briefly a selection of the more important sites in the county together with their ornithological significance. Details of lesser sites can be obtained from the B.T.O. or from K. Jones at 16 Lodge Road, Caerleon. For descriptive convenience the county has been divided into four geographical areas which are:

1. The Coastal Plain, comprising mainly reclaimed land below the 16 metre contour and used mainly as pasture. This region is heavily watched and has the highest density of registered sites.

2. The Central and Eastern region, comprising mainly mixed agricultural land and only rarely rising above about 300 metres. Observation is concentrated in the west of the area (around the Usk valley) and is particularly thin in the sector north of a line between Abergavenny and Monmouth.

Clive Landen   *Plate 1.* GOLDCLIFF POINT. One of the best places on the Gwent coast for observing bird migration. The posts in the background are used to support baskets (putchers) for catching salmon.

Bill Keen

Plate 2. THE SKIRRID FAWR, seen from the north-west. The "Holy Mountain" of local legend, it is separated from the main mass of the Black Mountains but is within the Brecon Beacons

3. The Western Coalfield, consisting of a mountainous area with industrialised valleys. Observation of this region is generally thin except for one or two localised areas and most of the registered sites are on its fringes.

4. The Black Mountains, a high, sparsely populated area with extensive heather moors and some forestry plantations.

THE COASTAL PLAIN

Peterstone Pill. Low-lying pasture drained by a network of reens into a rectangular basin (the Gout) which in turn, empties via valves in the sea-wall into the Severn. At low tide there are extensive mud-flats. The area has been designated a Site of Special Scientific Interest. Access is by public footpaths from the B4239 road and along the sea-wall. Its main importance is as a winter-feeding area for waders, principally Dunlin, Knot, Redshank, Ringed Plover and Grey Plover, and also duck, which regularly include substantial numbers of Shoveler and up to 20 Scaup and Common Scoter. A wide variety of birds occurs on passage and regularly includes Garganey, Little Ringed Plover, Whimbrel, Wood Sandpiper, Ruff and Little Stint. In common with most other coastal sites, Shelduck and Redshank breed.

Newport Docks. Extensive reed-beds with mud and some open water; may be visited with permission of British Rail. Its main importance is its sizeable colonies of Sedge and Reed Warblers.

Uskmouth. Extensive mud-flats with encroaching Spartina and nearby ashponds formed from settling fuel-ash slurry from the adjacent power station. Access is by permission from the power station authorities. The ashponds constitute one of the most important wader roosts in Gwent; in January 1974 they held the exceptional total of 17,700 birds which included 16,000 Dunlin and represented about 70% of the Gwent wader population at the time. Peak winter numbers are generally only about one third of this number and also include Lapwing, Ringed and Grey Plover, Redshank and Knot. Other waders occur on passage, including Whimbrel in spring and Godwits, Green Sandpiper, Greenshank and Ruff in autumn.

Goldcliff Point. Protrudes into the mouth of the Severn; access is by marked public footpaths. The commoner passerine species occur in fairly large numbers on passage. Offshore seabird passage is sparse comprising mainly small numbers of Terns. The nearby Pill can hold substantial numbers of passage waders, particularly Common Sandpiper.

Undy Foreshore. Saltmarsh with extensive mud-flats at low tide. Access is by footpaths to the sea-wall. Its main importance is both as a roost and a feeding area for winter wader flocks. This is usually the largest wader roost in Gwent and has held as many as 15,000 Dunlin. Other roosting species include Lapwing, Grey Plover, Turnstone, Curlew and Knot.

Spring and autumn passage is very similar to that at Peterstone Pill but with rather more Curlew Sandpiper and fewer Little Ringed Plover. As with most other coastal localities Short-eared Owl and Merlin often occur from autumn to spring and ' Grey ' Geese and Snow Bunting are occasional.

Magor Reserve. A sedge-peat bog, and the largest remnant of the formerly extensive Monmouthshire fenland. It is designated a Site of Special Scientific Interest and is owned by the Gwent Trust for Nature Conservation, from whom permission must be obtained for access. Its main ornithological importance is as a breeding site for wetland species which include Common Snipe, Redshank, Mallard, Reed Warbler, Sedge Warbler and in the recent past, Garganey. Woodcock and Green Sandpiper occur in autumn and a variety of ducks and waders together with Kingfisher are found in winter.

THE CENTRAL AND EASTERN AREAS

Llandegfedd Reservoir. A reservoir completed in 1963 and covering about 200 hectares (500 acres). Access is strictly by permission of the Welsh National Water Development Authority but commanding views are obtained from a hillside car park and picnic area. In its short history it has become one of the major wintering sites for wildfowl in Wales and regularly holds large numbers of Mallard, Teal, Wigeon, Pochard, Tufted Duck and Coot, and smaller numbers of Goosander, Goldeneye and Great Crested Grebe, Passage, which is good in both spring and autumn, commonly includes Arctic, Common and Black Terns and waders such as Green and Common Sandpipers.

Ynysyfro Reservoir. Two small reservoirs with a public footpath running between. It is the second most important site for wintering wildfowl in Gwent with numbers of Tufted Duck and Pochard often approaching those at Llandegfedd Reservoir. Black, Common and Arctic Terns occur on passage, as do waders, including Greenshank and Common and Green Sandpipers.

Pant-yr-eos Reservoir. A small reservoir enclosed by hills with steep, wooded slopes. Access is by public footpath to the woodland only, but with views over the reservoir. Numbers of wintering wildfowl are small but the adjacent deciduous and coniferous woodlands hold breeding Buzzard, Woodcock, Nightjar, Woodpeckers, Redstart, Lesser Whitethroat, Wood Warbler and Tree Pipit.

Wye Valley. Predominantly mixed woodland with limestone cliffs and outcrops, the whole valley has been designated an Area of Outstanding Natural Beauty. Several sites within it have been registered. It is certainly the most important breeding area for woodland birds in Gwent and holds, among all the more usual species, Heron, Hawfinch, Pied Flycatcher, and (until 1972) Nightingale, Crossbill commonly occurs in winter.

Wentwood. A large Forestry Commission area of over 1,000 hectares (2,500 acres), mainly of larch and spruce of varied ages but with remnants of older deciduous woodland, and also with other habitats, including a reservoir. It is well-furnished with footpaths, bridleways, car parks and picnic areas. The diversity of habitats is reflected in the large number (over 130) of species recorded. Breeding species include Buzzard, Sparrow-hawk, Kestrel, Woodcock, Barn, Tawny and Little Owls, Nightjar, Turtle Dove, Wood Warbler, Stonechat, Whinchat and Redstart, while other species which have been recorded with some regularity in summer, but not proved to have bred, comprise Golden Oriole, Siskin, Crossbill and, very recently, Firecrest. The reservoir holds small numbers of duck in winter, mainly Tufted Duck and Pochard.

Olway Meadow. One of a number of low-lying areas associated with the Usk; it comprises water meadows, which often flood in winter and are drained by reens lined with blackthorn and willow vegetation. Access is by permission of local land owners. This site and other similar areas support a high diversity of breeding birds which includes Mallard, Curlew, Snipe and Sand Martin. Waders, including Green Sandpiper and Greenshank occur on passage and moderate numbers of Bewick's Swans are regular winter visitors.

Abergavenny Sewage Works. An Usk valley site surrounded by water meadows and a small marsh. The sewage works attracts small numbers of passage waders in both spring and autumn, principally Green and Common Sandpiper and Redshank. In recent winters it has held Gwent's only Water Pipits. In the surrounding area Mallard, Mute Swan, Coot, Grey and Yellow Wagtails and Dipper all breed, while wintering species include Little Grebe, Water Rail, Jack Snipe, Kingfisher and Dipper.

Llanarth Court. One of the few well-documented sites in N.E. Gwent. It covers about 140 hectares (350 acres) and habitats include extensive parkland, arable and pasture land, both coniferous and deciduous wood-land and a small lake with reed beds. Access is strictly by permission of the owners. There is a very wide variety of breeding species which in 1969 included Cirl Bunting and at one location as many as eight species of warbler have been heard singing at the same time. There is a good diversity of woodland species in winter, together with Mallard, Teal and Common Snipe.

THE COALFIELD

Cwm Tyleri. A narrow steep-sided valley rising from about 200 to 530 m (650 to 1,700 ft.) with oak and larch woodland, rough grazing, a small reservoir and heather moor. Breeding birds include several species typical of uplands and sessile oak woodlands:— Red Grouse, Common Sandpiper, Redstart, Whinchat, Pied Flycatcher, Wood Warbler, Grey Wagtail, Dipper and Raven.

Lasgarn Wood. Mixed but predominantly oak woodland rising to heather moor. Typical high woodland species breed and the Red Grouse which breed on the moor at 425 m (*c* 1,400 ft.) form the most southerly natural population in Britain.

Pen-y-Fan Pond. A small reservoir surrounded by upland grazing and scattered trees. Access is by public footpath and good views can be obtained from the road. The reservoir often holds small numbers of Tufted Duck and Pochard in winter, but the main importance of the area is its variety of upland and other breeding species.

Garnlydan Reservoir. The largest of several small reservoirs at elevations above 400 m (1,300 ft.) on the northern edge of the coalfield. It is surrounded by heather moor, and Mallard, Lapwing, Snipe, Curlew, Common Sandpiper, Dunlin and Red Grouse all breed in the vicinity. Small numbers of diving ducks are generally present in winter, and passage, though generally very light, has on occasion involved large numbers of hirundines and has included a variety of waders, notably Turnstone and Whimbrel.

Trefil Quarries. Another site on the northern fringe of the coalfield comprising limestone quarries surrounded by heather moor similar to Garnlydan. Birds breeding in the area include Red Grouse, Common Snipe, Common Sandpiper, Ring Ouzel and Wheatear.

THE BLACK MOUNTAINS

Three sites have been registered in this area and all are basically similar mountain areas with high moors, deep valleys, fast-flowing streams and oak woodland. Their main ornithological importance is their wide variety of upland breeding species which includes Common Sandpiper, Raven, Dipper, Ring Ouzel, Redstart, Wood Warbler, Pied Flycatcher, Grey Wagtail and, on the summits, Red Grouse.

Acknowledgements. Thanks must be given to all those field workers who gave up so much of their time to visit sites, particularly K. D. Bradley, T. G. Evans, R. G. Hannington, S. N. G. Howells, R. & L. Johnstone, M. G. Kelsey, B. C. Lewis, J. M. S. Lewis, A. Moxley, B. Phelps, S. Smith, C. Titcombe, T. S. Toombs and M. Tranter.

CHAPTER 3

BREEDING BIRDS 1968-72

by W. G. Lewis and P. N. Ferns

AS part of the British Trust for Ornithology/Irish Wildbird Conservancy Atlas project, the breeding birds of Gwent were surveyed during the five breeding seasons from 1968 to 1972. The national results of the project have already been published (Sharrock, 1976), but as it is difficult to identify specific squares on a map of the whole of the British Isles, larger scale versions of the Gwent results are presented here for 63 species. Details of the remaining 59 species of confirmed or possible breeding birds in the county are included in a list at the end of this chapter. The latter species either occurred in only one square or were absent from just one or two.

The Atlas project employed the 10 km squares of the British grid as its basic recording unit throughout England, Wales and Scotland. The letter and number designations of each of these squares are shown on the first map of the series displayed on the following pages. The meaning of the different sized dots employed on these maps is as follows.

Large dot — confirmed breeding. Indicated by—
occupied or previously occupied nest; adult entering or leaving nest site; recently fledged young; adult carrying food for young or faecal sac, or giving distraction display; eggshell found.

Medium dot — probable breeding. Indicated by —
adult holding territory, nest-building, visiting probable nest site or behaving anxiously; singing male present (or breeding calls heard) on more than one date in the same place; courtship and display observed; brood patch on trapped female.

Small dot — possible breeding. Indicated by —
bird observed in nesting habitat during breeding season.

With its total of 118 species of confirmed breeding birds, Gwent has rather more than the neighbouring counties of Glamorgan (115), Brecknock (111), Hereford (107) and Gloucestershire (106), but rather fewer than Somerset (125). This is a remarkably high total considering the small size of the county relative to these others and demonstrates the considerable diversity of habitats found within its borders. It should be

9

emphasized, however, that county boundaries do not follow 10 km grid lines, and that in arriving at county totals from Atlas results, no account is taken of the exact position of breeding records within 10 km squares that happen to straddle county borders. Although Dunlin, Black-headed Gull and Tufted Duck are included in the Gwent Atlas squares the actual sites involved lie outside the county.

For a detailed discussion of the national distribution of each species, the reader is referred to Sharrock (1976), but it is worth briefly mentioning one or two features which are important in understanding the distribution of breeding birds in Gwent. First of all the county is situated at the edge of the upland region which occupies most of central Wales. Thus a number of species which are characteristic of such regions, e.g. Merlin, Red Grouse, Golden Plover and Ring Ouzel, do breed in the county but only in the north-west. On the other hand, species such as Red-legged Part-ridge, Nightingale and Cirl Bunting which are largely restricted to the lowlands of south and east England, do penetrate as far as Gwent at the very edge of their range. The county also has good sized breeding popula-tions of Buzzard, Raven and Pied Flycatcher — species which are quite abundant in Wales, Scotland and the south-west of England, but which are uncommon in the south-east. It also has a number of coastal and coastal-fringe species, such as Shelduck, Oystercatcher, Ringed Plover, Redshank and Rock Pipit. Some species are dependent upon still or running fresh water, and their distribution within the county is thus restricted to such areas. Amongst these are Great Crested Grebe, Little Grebe, Garganey, Canada Goose, Mute Swan, Water Rail, Moorhen, Coot, Common Sandpiper, Kingfisher, Dipper, Grey Wagtail and Reed Warbler. A few species are patchily distributed because of some other specific habitat requirement, e.g. Nightjar, Hawfinch and Crossbill.

Finally, there are one or two rare species which are worthy of further mention. Gwent contained the only breeding Wigeon in the whole of Wales in 1968–72. This species is a somewhat irregular breeder in the southern part of Britain, and as a result it is often suggested that such records may be due to escapes from captive wildfowl collections. The Gwent record refers to Newport Docks and is based on reports by a wild-fowler during four consecutive breeding seasons. The Marsh Warbler is an extremely uncommon breeding bird throughout Britain, yet we are lucky enough to have at least an occasional pair nesting in Gwent. The Severn valley has always been regarded as a stronghold of this elusive species, and the largest concentration of breeding birds in 1968–72 was found in the Worcester area. The Golden Oriole is an even rarer breeding species, with confirmed nesting in only five 10 km squares throughout the country. Gwent has a record of probable breeding at Wentwood, though this has unfortunately been omitted from the national Atlas map (Sharrock, 1976). There is, incidentally, at least one further mistake in the national maps which concern Gwent. The Woodlark record from the west of the county is a confirmed breeding record (as in the map shown here) and not a probable record. The records of probable breeding of

10

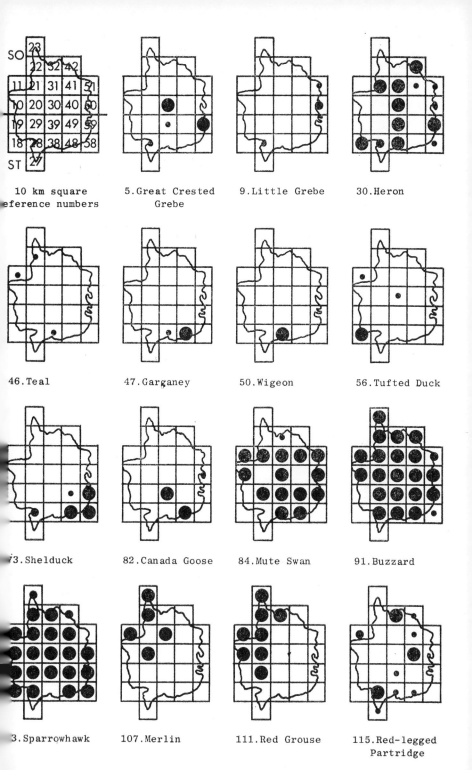

10 km square reference numbers

5. Great Crested Grebe

9. Little Grebe

30. Heron

46. Teal

47. Garganey

50. Wigeon

56. Tufted Duck

73. Shelduck

82. Canada Goose

84. Mute Swan

91. Buzzard

3. Sparrowhawk

107. Merlin

111. Red Grouse

115. Red-legged Partridge

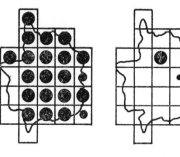

116. Partridge

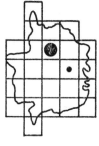

117. Quail

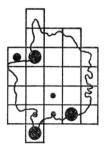

120. Water Rail

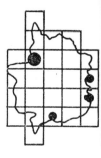

125. Corncrake

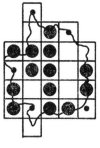

127. Coot

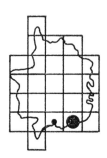

131. Oystercatcher

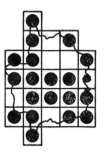

133. Lapwing

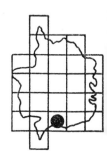

134. Ringed Plov

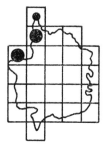

140. Golden Plover

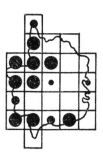

145. Snipe

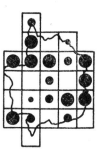

148. Woodcock

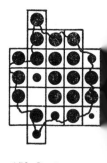

150. Curlew

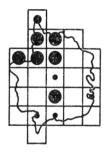

159. Common Sand-
piper

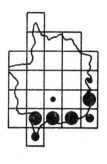

161. Redshank

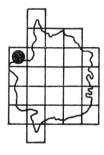

178. Dunlin

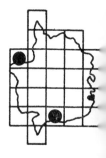

199. Lesser Bla
backed Gull

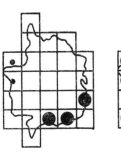

200.Herring Gull

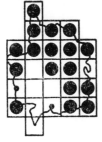

232.Stock Dove

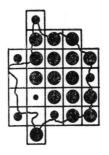

235.Turtle Dove

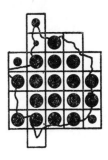

235a.Collared
Dove

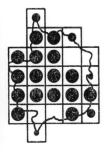

241.Barn Owl

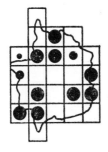

252.Nightjar

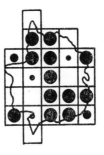

264.Lesser Spotted
Woodpecker

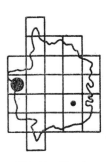

271.Woodlark

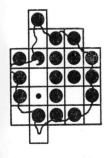

277.Sand Martin

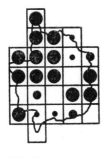

279.Raven

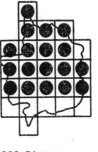

300.Dipper

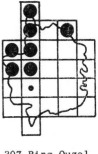

307.Ring Ouzel

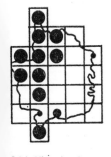

311.Wheatear

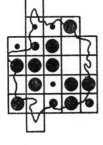

317.Stonechat

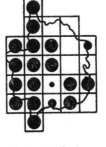

318.Whinchat

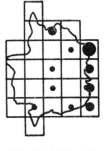

322.Nightingale

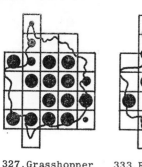

327. Grasshopper
Warbler

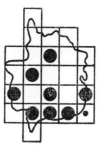

333. Reed Warbler

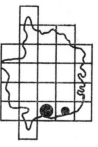

334. Marsh Warbler

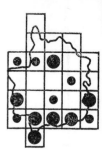

337. Sedge Warbler

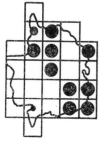

348. Lesser White-
throat

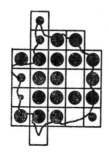

357. Wood Warbler

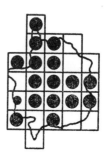

368. Pied Fly-
catcher

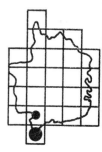

379. Rock Pipit

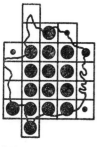

382. Yellow Wag-
tail

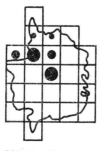

391. Hawfinch

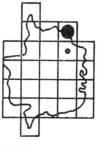

394. Siskin

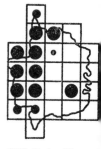

397. Redpoll

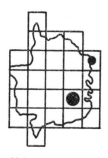

404. Crossbill

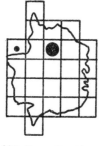

410. Corn Bunting

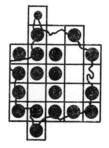

421. Reed Bunting

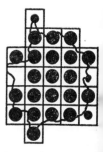

425. Tree Sparrow

Hobby, Long-eared Owl and Cirl Bunting are, however, correct. It is up to all of us to ensure that everything possible is done to promote the survival of all of these rarer species, by both preserving their habitats and protecting them from disturbance.

H. W. Hamar was Regional Atlas Organiser in 1968 and 1969, and W. G. Lewis from 1970 onwards. The Gwent maps were constructed by K. Jones, the final versions being drawn and the text written by P. .N Ferns. None of the Atlas results would have been possible without the dedication and enthusiasm of workers in the field. Considerable help with bordering squares and in the collation of results was given by the recorders in adjacent counties — H. Morrey Salmon, A. Heathcote, S. F. Young (Glamorgan); M. V. Preece (Brecknock); R. H. Baillie, A. J. Smith (Hereford); P. Dymott (Gloucestershire).

SPECIES RECORDED IN 1968 - 72, BUT NOT SHOWN ON THE MAPS

A. BREEDING CONFIRMED IN ALL SQUARES

234.	Woodpigeon	308.	Blackbird
255.	Swift	325.	Robin
272.	Skylark	346.	Garden Warbler
274.	Swallow	356.	Chiffchaff
280.	Carrion Crow	366.	Spotted Flycatcher
283.	Jackdaw	371.	Dunnock
284.	Magpie	380.	Pied Wagtail
286.	Jay	392.	Greenfinch
288.	Great Tit	393.	Goldfinch
289.	Blue Tit	401.	Bullfinch
299.	Wren	407.	Chaffinch
301.	Mistle Thrush	409.	Yellowhammer
303.	Song Thrush	424.	House Sparrow

B. BREEDING CONFIRMED IN ALL SQUARES EXCEPT ONE OR TWO (AT MOST FOUR)

45.	Mallard	293.	Willow Tit
110.	Kestrel	296.	Nuthatch
118.	Pheasant	298.	Treecreeper
126.	Moorhen	320.	Redstart
237.	Cuckoo	343.	Blackcap
246.	Little Owl	347.	Whitethroat
247.	Tawny Owl	354.	Willow Warbler
258.	Kingfisher	364.	Goldcrest
262.	Green Woodpecker	373.	Meadow Pipit
263.	Great Spotted Woodpecker	376.	Tree Pipit
276.	House Martin	381.	Grey Wagtail
282.	Rook	389.	Starling
290.	Coal Tit	395.	Linnet
292.	Marsh Tit		

C. PRESENT ONLY IN ONE SQUARE

104.	Hobby	Probable breeding in	SO11
198.	Great Black-backed Gull	Confirmed breeding in	ST48
208.	Black-headed Gull	Probable breeding in	SO11
248.	Long-eared Owl	Probable breeding in	ST18
278.	Golden Oriole	Probable breeding in	ST49
415.	Cirl Bunting	Probable breeding in	SO31

CHAPTER 4

COASTAL BIRDS

by W. A. VENABLES AND K. JONES

AT a conservative estimate, the coastline of mainland Britain is about 4,000 miles in length. Much of it is estuarine and in winter it is warmed by the waters of the Gulf Stream. These features combine to make the British coast very attractive as a wintering area for many birds, particularly waders and wildfowl.

Most of these birds are found in the estuaries and in a typical winter Britain holds over half of the waders present on the Atlantic coasts of Europe and North Africa, including internationally important concentrations of Turnstone, Curlew, Bar-tailed Godwit, Redshank, Knot, Dunlin and Sanderling. They also hold half (sometimes even more) of the Shelduck and two-fifths of the Wigeon wintering in N.W. Europe. The figures for geese are even more dramatic, with British estuaries holding substantial proportions of the world populations of several species, including about two-thirds of the world's dark-bellied Brent Geese and the entire Greenland and Spitzbergen breeding populations of the Barnacle Goose. The numbers of Bewick's and Whooper Swans using British estuaries are also internationally important.

As such large numbers of birds depend upon our estuaries, the increasing number of schemes to develop them in ways which would eliminate or severely reduce intertidal mudflats, for example the building of barrages, are particularly disturbing.

The purpose of the Birds of Estuaries Enquiry (1969–75), which was organised by the British Trust for Ornithology in conjunction with the Wildfowl Trust and the Royal Society for the Protection of Birds, was to determine, as accurately as possible, the numbers and variety of birds which are dependent upon British estuaries and in what ways they use them; e.g. whether as "refuelling stations" on passage migrations, or as feeding areas, or both; and whether particular areas within an estuary are more important than others, either generally or for particular species or activities. Armed with such information it would be possible to make a reasoned prediction of the impact that a proposed estuarine development scheme would have on the bird population of the estuary, if it were implemented.

The enquiry took the form of a series of monthly counts in which all British estuaries were covered on the same day, usually the Sunday nearest to the highest spring tide of each month. Results were collected by local organisers and forwarded to the B.T.O. The first phase of the enquiry ended in 1975 and the results, which are still being analysed, will serve as a baseline with which future counts can be compared.

The remainder of this chapter deals with the results of the *Birds of Estuaries Enquiry* which were obtained on the Gwent coast. For descriptive purposes the coast is divided into two regions, one starting at the western county boundary and running through Peterstone and St. Brides Wentlooge to the Usk estuary (the Peterstone–Uskmouth stretch), and the other starting at the eastern shore of the Usk estuary and running through Undy and Caldicot to the eastern county boundary (the Uskmouth–Wye stretch). Unfortunately, it was not until the last two years of the survey (1973/74 and 1974/75) that the Peterstone–Uskmouth stretch was counted as part of the enquiry, and for this reason, the results presented in detail here are generally confined to these two years in which coverage was complete.

WADERS

Waders were counted only at high tide. This took advantage of the fact that during the period of the *Estuaries Enquiry* the vast bulk of Gwent's waders used only two high-tide roosts, one at the ash-ponds of Uskmouth Power Station and the other on saltmarsh near Collister Pill. Thus an estimate of the total numbers arriving at or leaving these roosts, generally accounted for over 80 % of the county population. The remaining, and much smaller roosts, were located and counted by observers walking the coastal footpath. This latter method of observation was also used to count the bulk of the Curlew, Whimbrel and Lapwing populations, as these species tended to avoid the main roosts and to spend the high-tide period in fields behind the sea-wall. Observers on the coastal path also noted the size, direction of movement, and time of passing of large wader flocks and these were often correlated with arrivals at the roosts. The main gap in the coastal coverage was around Redwick, near the western end of the Uskmouth-Wye stretch, but available data suggest that very few waders are found in this region at high tide.

Results

All Waders. Table 1 shows the peak counts for Gwent during the last four years of the *Estuaries Enquiry*. These counts are the totals of the highest counts in each year for each species, regardless of the month in which they occurred. For example, the 1974/75 figure includes the peak Whimbrel count of 300 in May and the peak Dunlin count of 15,000 in January. The peak count represents a minimum estimate of the total number of waders which used the Gwent coast during a particular year. To illustrate the importance of the Gwent coast relative to the Severn estuary as a whole, or to the coasts of Wales or Britain, peak counts (where available) for these areas have also been included in Table 1. These latter figures have been calculated from the data given by Prater (1974; 1975; 1976).

18

TABLE 1. *Peak wader counts*

	1971/72	1972/73	1973/74	1974/75
Gwent coast	16,000	21,000	43,200	23,100
Severn estuary	75,500	83,300	124,800	n.a.
Welsh estuaries	91,300	107,800	142,000	n.a.
British estuaries	1,440,000	1,260,000	1,450,000	n.a.

Severn estuary totals comprise counts of the Gwent, Gloucestershire, Avon and Somerset coasts and the Taff/Ely estuary (S. Glamorgan). Welsh estuaries totals include counts of the north bank of the Severn estuary and the west bank of the Dee.

n.a. = not available at time of writing.

Individual Species. Under each of the species headings below, all tabulated data refer to the numbers of birds counted on the Gwent coast as part of the *Estuaries Enquiry*. Numbers in brackets (in the tables) indicate counts which were not made on scheduled days but which are considered to be more representative of the local population in that period than the scheduled count. Numbers which appear in brackets after the name of each species are the combined counts (made in January unless otherwise indicated) for Welsh estuaries (W.E.) and British estuaries (Br.E.) in the year 1973/74.

Oystercatcher (*W.E. 26,400; Br.E. 169,700*)

	1971/72	1972/73	1973/74	1974/75
Highest Count	31	(20)	(17)	60
Month	April	April	April	February

Being for the most part mud, the Gwent coast is not a very suitable feeding area for this species and this is reflected in the low counts obtained. Highest numbers generally occurred in April on the Peterstone–Uskmouth stretch and presumably involved birds on spring passage.

Lapwing. (*W.E. 17,800; Br.E. 124,400*)

	J	A	S	O	N	D	J	F	M	A	M	J
1973/74	300	890	1,160	1,180	890	2,430	2,970	810	400	20	100	360
1974/75	400	900	1,000+	220	100	70	1,020	240	70	10	20	400

This species tends to spend the high-tide period in fields behind the sea-wall, so most were counted by the coastal walkers. Flocks were generally distributed along the entire coastal stretch (as they also were when feeding on the shore at low tide) and the highest numbers occurred in winter and on autumn passage. As the Lapwing is to a large extent an inland species, even in winter, the counts fall well short of the total county population which in January 1974 was certainly in excess of 7,000.

19

Ringed Plover. (*W.E. 1,100; Br.E. 7,700*)

	J	A	S	O	N	D	J	F	M	A	M	J
1973/74	30	840	950	60	150	12	910	140	20	210	620	210
1974/75	11	1,220	740	130	140	(45)	6	100	(10)	70	50	40

Most birds were counted at the major roosts. As in the rest of Britain, maximum numbers usually occur in autumn as Arctic breeders move south, and the 910 in January 1974 was most exceptional. The total of 950 in September 1973 represented about 5% of the British population at that time, and 42% of the Welsh population.

Grey Plover. (*W.E. 1,000; Br.E. 12,100*)

	J	A	S	O	N	D	J	F	M	A	M	J
1973/74	19	60	130	110	480	390	470	210	230	80	95	20
1974/75	26	65	20	75	310	300	260	350	50	15	(6)	4

Most birds were counted at the major roosts. Maximum numbers occurred in winter when the totals approached 50% of the Welsh population and as much as 1% of the total European population. The main feeding area for this species was the Uskmouth–Wye stretch, particularly Uskmouth to Magor Pill.

Golden Plover. (*W.E. 3,800; Br.E. 41,200*). Large flocks of up to 3,000 birds were present at Undy throughout the winter of 1970/71. In subsequent years, however, it occurred only erratically in Gwent with numbers seldom reaching double figures, though most exceptionally, 300 were counted in December 1973. Like the Lapwing, this is not a principally estuarine species and large numbers spend the winter far inland (not usually in Gwent).

Turnstone. (*W.E. 1,100; Br. E. 10,200*)

	J	A	S	O	N	D	J	F	M	A	M	J
1971/72	30	50	100	10	30	60	50	60	200	350	350	59
1972/73	3	1	40	10	40	60	100	100	60	300	300	150
1973/74	30	31	15	43	75	33	110	100	100	60	91	60
1974/75	50	40	32	75	19	56	75	40	40	40	2	20

Most birds were counted at the major roosts. Counts for 1971/72 and 1972/73 are given here in full because, despite the incomplete cover of the county, highest numbers in these years were much above those in subsequent years. These high numbers resulted, for the most part, from a very marked spring passage which was not recorded again in 1973/74 or 1974/75. Suitable feeding areas for this species are few, but despite this, the January population for Gwent was on average about 8% of the total counted in Welsh estuaries.

Common Snipe. (*W.E. 150; Br.E. 2,900*).   This is another mainly inland species which does not move to estuaries in large numbers during the type of mild winter which has prevailed throughout the *Estuaries Enquiry*. Apart from totals of 115 in January 1973 and 107 in December 1973 counts along the Gwent coast seldom reached double figures.

Curlew. (*W.E. 6,900; Br.E. 56,300*)

	J	A	S	O	N	D	J	F	M	A	M	J
1973/74	200	390	410	270	370	330	590	350	430	370	120	80
1974/75	210	410	510	300	200	250	330	480	300	100	20	120

Although its size made it unlikely that this species would be missed by counters, the scattered distribution of its high-tide roosts, together with the tendency for their locations to vary, made a thorough search essential. Favoured feeding areas also tended to vary. The highest numbers occurred in autumn and winter, and the 1973/74 January count represented about 8½% of the total in Welsh estuaries. The highest monthly counts in the last four years of the *Enquiry* were 495, 400, 590 and 510, so allowing for incomplete coverage in the first two years, the Gwent population appears to have been very stable.

Whimbrel. (*Br.E. 2,000 (May)*)

	J	A	S	O	N	D	J	F	M	A	M	J
1973/74	10	37	2	—	—	—	—	—	—	10	140	5
1974/75	12	41	6	—	—	—	—	—	—	(250)	(300)	7

Counting presented problems, as on most parts of the coast the birds spent high-tide periods feeding in scattered flocks in coastal fields. Feeding on the shore was usually confined to the region immediately below the high-tide mark. It was recorded mainly on passage, with higher numbers in spring than in autumn, and with peak counts in early May. In spring, the Severn estuary usually holds an extremely large proportion of British Whimbrel — apart from the Gwent birds, between 1,000 and 2,000 have been recorded from the Somerset coast in each of the last four years of the *Estuaries Enquiry*, and may well have been present in earlier years also. It seems likely that the Severn estuary is the most important passage station in Britain for this species.

Black-tailed Godwit. (*W.E. 700*; Br.E. 3,500*). *This figure for the Welsh estuaries population represents an average for the four winters, 1971–74. (The 1973/74 figure of 2 is very untypical). Nevertheless, Black-tailed Godwit is still a very scarce species in Wales during winter, and the western bank of the Dee estuary carries almost the entire January population. On counts of the Gwent coast it was regularly recorded in most months outside the winter period, but usually in numbers of less than ten and only twice above twenty.

Bar-tailed Godwit. (*W.E. 1,700; Br.E. 51,800*). It was not recorded on the winter counts, but like the last species, occurred regularly on spring, summer and autumn counts, generally in very small numbers, but with noticeable passage peaks in May (once April) of 23 (1972), 58 (1973), 72 (1974) and 38 (1975). The British population as a whole is at its lowest in spring, but even so, the peak Gwent counts represent less than 1% of the British total for this time of year.

Redshank. (*W.E. 4,600; Br.E. 66,900*).

	J	A	S	O	N	D	J	F	M	A	M	J
1973/74	300	420	400	240	680	370	370	220	700	240	280	94
1974/75	490	400	600	380	350	400	400	84	140	150	10	220

The vast majority of birds were counted at the Uskmouth and Caldicot roosts, with less than 10% of the total at other localities. The month of the highest count varied greatly over the last four years of the *Estuaries Enquiry* and in most there was more than one peak. The January count for 1973/74 represented about 7% of the Welsh estuaries count and 0.4% of the British estuaries count.

Knot. (*W.E. 13,100; Br.E. 279,500*).

	J	A	S	O	N	D	J	F	M	A	M	J
1971/72	110	26	3	3,000	3,000	4,000	950	3,000	500	150	22	—
1972/73	—	—	27	5,000	3,000	400	2,400	4,000	500	60	12	—
1973/74	7	12	280	4	2,000	13,200	6,100	6,200	320	180	34	26
1974/75	34	35	80	100	100	1,100	2,000	3,800	170	250	13	9

Even in 1973/74 and 1974/75 when coastal cover was complete almost all birds were counted at the Uskmouth and Caldicot roosts. For this reason full figures for 1971/72 and 1972/73 are included here, as the failure to count the Peterstone–Uskmouth stretch in these years would have had little effect upon totals. Maximum numbers occurred in the winter months and the January count for 1973/74 represented, respectively, almost 50% of the Welsh, and about 2% of the British populations. The December count of that winter (13,200) was as high as 5% of the British count.

Dunlin. (*W.E. 58,000; Br.E. 621,000*).

	J	A	S	O	N	D
1973/74	2,000	3,800	5,500	8,100	14,800	17,200
1974/75	3,900	3,000	2,000	9,000	14,800	10,500
	J	F	M	A	M	J
1973/74	23,500	17,200	11,100	10,000	12,700	140
1974/75	15,000	14,000	7,000	7,100	8,000	40

Most birds were counted at the main Uskmouth and Caldicot roosts. Feeding birds, however, are much more dispersed with about a third of the total using the Peterstone–Uskmouth stretch. Numbers were highest in winter, but spring passage of Arctic breeders was very significant in late April and early May. The January count for Gwent in 1973/74 represented 41% of the Welsh total, 4% of the British total and about 1% of the European population.

Other Waders. Several species were recorded in small numbers, mainly on passage. These were (maximum counts and months in which they occurred are in parentheses): Little Ringed Plover (1, April—October), Jack Snipe (1, January—February), Green Sandpiper (7, August), Wood Sandpiper (1, September), Common Sandpiper (*c*20, August), Spotted Redshank (8, August), Greenshank (8, August), Little Stint (2, July—October), Curlew Sandpiper (6, August), Sanderling (*c*30, May) and Ruff (5 August).

WILDFOWL

Of the wildfowl, only ducks are recorded in significant numbers on the Gwent coast. Counting at high tide on the scheduled days generally proved unsatisfactory for the estimation of duck numbers for two reasons: firstly, because most species tended to fly out into the estuary at high tide, often beyond the limits of visibility from the shore, and secondly, because from September to February certain coastal stretches were subject to continual disturbance from shooting at weekends Consequently, in the many cases where unscheduled weekday counts. have exceeded scheduled weekend counts, the former have been used here as a more realistic indication of the numbers present. In practice, Peterstone Wentlooge was routinely counted on the Friday preceding the scheduled count.

For ducks other than Wigeon and Shelduck, Peterstone Wentlooge was by far the most important counting station on the Gwent coast. Consequently, counts prior to 1973/74, when this area was not covered, are particularly inaccurate and have generally not been considered here.

23

Results

Under each of the species headings below, all tabulated data refer to counts made on the Gwent coast as part of the *Estuaries Enquiry*. In the case of wildfowl counts, (unlike waders) totals for individual species in the Severn estuary as a whole were readily obtainable, as also were 1974/75 totals for Welsh estuaries. As a result, Severn estuary totals (S.E.) have been included for comparison, and both these and the Welsh estuaries totals (W.E.) are averages of the figures for the two years 1973/74 and 1974/75. It should also be noted that the British populations quoted (Br.) are estimates of the total populations for the country, including, where significant, inland counts. All such data referring to larger regions than Gwent are based on January counts and were obtained from Prater (1974; 1975; 1976) or from G. Atkinson-Willes (pers. comm.).

Mallard. *(S.E. 1,700; W.E. 2,100; Br. 400,000).*

	J	A	S	O	N	D	J	F	M	A	M	J
1973/74	170	290	180	510	140	760	340	84	240	110	210	470
1974/75	410	370	350	370	99	74	26	120	78	24	110	290

Overall, more than 80% of Mallard on the Gwent coast were counted at Peterstone Wentlooge. Winter numbers were much higher in 1973/74 than in 1974/75. Although there were no official *Estuaries Enquiry* counts at Peterstone in previous years, the personal records of the authors tend to indicate that the lower numbers were more typical of the winters from 1971 to 1975 as a whole. Nevertheless, the peak winter count of 760 in December 1973 represented nearly one quarter of the total counted in Welsh estuaries that month and about 30% of the total in the Severn estuary.

Summer and autumn numbers at Peterstone have been much more consistent than winter numbers over the past several years and have usually provided the peak count of the year. A peak in this period is common to other parts of the Severn estuary, with up to about 2,500 being counted in recent years. This may mean that the Severn estuary is an important local moulting ground for the species.

Teal. *(S.E. 390; W.E. 1,800; Br. 75,000).*

	J	A	S	O	N	D	J	F	M	A	M	J
1973/74	—	66	51	67	36	340	140	2	15	29	4	3
1974/75	1	55	11	5	11	5	18	130	18	6	—	—

Overall, more than 90% of Teal along the Gwent coast were counted at Peterstone Wentlooge. The highest counts, which were in December and January of 1973/74 and in February of 1974/75 represented 10—15% of the total Welsh estuaries counts at those times, and 27—70% of the

24

Severn estuary counts. Although numbers wintering in the Severn do not seem very high in themselves, it must be taken into consideration that the highest counts for Britain are seldom above 50,000, and the total of 1,000 in the Severn estuary in December 1973 was about 2% of this figure.

Wigeon. (*S.E. 5,400; W.E. 7,400; Br. 200,000*).

	J	A	S	O	N	D	J	F	M	A	M	J
1973/74	5	5	6	50	20	160	63	13	11	8	—	—
1974/75	—	—	3	10	150	110	210	29	32	—	—	—

Overall, nearly 90% of Wigeon were counted in the Undy region. Because of this, counts made in 1971/72 and 1972/73 are of value and maxima for these years were 350 (October) and 40 (December) respectively. The average peak count for 1971 to 1975 is about 190 which represents only 2.5%—3.5% of both the Severn and Welsh estuaries counts, and less than 0.1% of the British January population.

Shoveler. (*S.E. 190; W.E. 170; Br. 30,000*).

	J	A	S	O	N	D	J	F	M	A	M	J
1973/74	—	—	8	16	68	160	110	68	1	—	—	1
1974/75	1	2	7	21	61	47	50	—	—	2	—	—

This species was virtually unrecorded outside the Peterstone–Uskmouth stretch. In addition to the 1973/74 and 1974/75 maxima of 160 and 61, other records (Venables, 1974) indicate a maximum of 130 (January) in 1972/73, which gives an average of about 120 for the three winters. This represents about two-thirds of the average January counts for both Severn and Welsh estuaries, and about 0.4% of the total British population.

Scaup. (*Br. 24,000*).

	J	A	S	O	N	D	J	F	M	A	M	J
1973/74	2	—	2	6	11	20	—	9	—	3	4	—
1974/75	—	2	—	3	—	9	1	—	—	2	—	—

All birds were counted at Peterstone Wentlooge and were the only records for the entire Severn estuary. In 1973/74 there were no records in other Welsh estuaries either, but in 1974/75 up to 21 were counted in the Burry Inlet, and Hope Jones and Davis (1975) list small flocks at other places. Though it is not possible to give a realistic figure, the Gwent birds certainly represent a very high proportion of the Welsh estuary population, but the latter is itself less than 0.5% of the British total.

Common Scoter. (*W.E. 58; Br. 30-50,000*).

	J	A	S	O	N	D	J	F	M	A	M	J
1973/74	4	4	—	28	4	2	—	—	—	—	—	—
1974/75	7	5	—	1	25	24	13	16	11	13	1	—

With one exception of 20 at Undy in 1973 all records of this species were on the Peterstone–Uskmouth stretch, and as with Scaup, there were no records elsewhere in the Severn estuary. The larger Gwent totals were all about one-third of the combined Welsh estuaries counts in the same periods. However, this is a very marine species and the bulk of the Welsh winter population occurs outside estuaries on the open sea. For example, surveys of Carmarthen Bay from the air or from boats during 1974 indicated that numbers there may have been as high as 25,000 in March and 10–12,000 in September.

Shelduck. (*S.E. 1,700; W.E. 1,600; Br. 60,000*).

	J	A	S	O	N	D	J	F	M	A	M	J
1973/74	180	83	66	72	140	72	190	140	300	410	280	440
1974/75	470	74	180	79	150	120	100	190	370	290	76	600

Overall, about 70% of Shelduck were counted on the Uskmouth–Wye stretch (most at Undy) and 30% on the Peterstone–Uskmouth stretch (most at Peterstone Wentlooge). Each year shows two distinct peaks — one in spring, the other in summer — the first of which comprised mainly birds at Peterstone and the second, mainly birds at Undy. Numbers at both localities were lowest in late summer and autumn. As available counts for the April–July period are very incomplete for other localities in the Severn, and also for most other estuaries, it is not possible to put the Gwent peaks in a comparative context. However, the average January total is about 9% of the Welsh total and about 0.25% of the British population, which in turn, is about half of the N.W. European population.

In the two years considered here, the counts for the entire Severn estuary varied enormously from 2,990 in January 1974 (about 5% of the British total) to as low as 420 in January 1975.

The largest concentrations of this species in the Severn estuary are found in Bridgwater Bay in late summer and autumn (July–October), where as many as 5,000 gather to moult. The June–July build-up at Undy may be connected with this latter concentration at Bridgwater Bay.

Other Ducks. Several species occurred irregularly and in very small numbers. These were (with size of maximum count and its month): Garganey (5, August), Gadwall (7, August), Pintail (13, January), Tufted Duck (9, January), Goldeneye (1, February) and Red-breasted Merganser (1, several months, April–October).

26

GULLS

Table 2 shows the combined counts for the Gwent coast during the two years when complete coverage was achieved. In numerous cases where the scheduled count was known to be unrepresentative (generally owing to limits imposed on observation by poor weather conditions) it has been supplemented by other counts made in the same period.

With the exception of the Great Black-backed Gull, all species feed and roost inland to a large extent, which means that the *Estuaries Enquiry* counts do not give an estimate of the county population. Additionally, as the proportion of the county population actually present in the estuary varies with time of day, height of tide, and probably whether or not sewers are discharging, the counts cannot be relied upon as an accurate indication of the total numbers of gulls making use of the estuary. As an illustration of the former point, in February 1975, when 180 Herring Gulls were recorded on the estuary count, 1,200 were counted at Newport tip and a further 290 at Cwmbran tip. Additionally, in the latter part of 1975, 3,350 were counted at Newport tip, 1,000 at Llandegfedd Reservoir and 1,200 at Ebbw Vale tip. Counts made during 1974/75 by G. Mudge of University College, Cardiff, at the estuaries of the Taff, Rhymney and Usk, on the islands of Flat Holm and Steep Holm, and at numerous inland reservoirs and tips, have produced the following figures which probably give a fairly good indication of the total winter gull populations for the whole of the north side of the Severn estuary:

Lesser Black-backed Gull	950
Herring Gull	17,490
Common Gull	1,020
Black-headed Gull	32,650
Total Gulls	52,110

OTHER GROUPS OF BIRDS

The only species which occurred regularly along the Gwent coast were Heron and Cormorant, both in small numbers which seldom exceeded ten.

GENERAL DISCUSSION

At the Fifth International Conference on the Conservation of Wetlands and Waterfowl, at Heiligenhafen in 1974, a series of criteria which could be used to determine whether a wetland is of international importance was agreed. In the case of waders, two of these criteria are that it should support a total of 20,000 or more birds, or 1 % or more of the European total for any particular species. The Gwent shore, with its

TABLE 2. *Monthly counts of gulls along the Gwent coast*

		J	A	S	O	N	D	J	F	M	A	M	J
Great Black-backed Gull	1973/74	—	5	18	33	8	8	14	2	—	2	4	3
	1974/75	16	12	31	—	2	3	1	2	1	—	—	3
Lesser Black-backed Gull	1973/74	—	—	23	15	100	30	34	—	—	—	31	20
	1974/75	37	51	6	—	3	16	7	30	12	—	4	20
Herring Gull	1973/74	24	8	6	200	210	30	350	51	230	310	350	250
	1974/75	360	430	320	160	10	94	110	180	60	52	82	70
Common Gull	1973/74	—	—	1	2	2	10	2	—	2	44	79	5
	1974/75	3	70	—	—	50	5	500	370	120	80	240	—
Black-headed Gull	1973/74	700	1,000	1,410	150	650	840	12,500	880	600	450	62	680
	1974/75	1,240	5,780	850	3,210	1,180	990	1,000	2,300	1,600	800	39	180
TOTAL GULLS	1973/74	720	1,010	1,460	400	970	920	12,900	430	840	750	570	960
	1974/75	1,650	6,340	1,210	3,370	1,340	1,110	1,620	2,880	1,790	930	370	270

peak counts of 43,200 in 1973/74 and 23,100 in 1974/75 (Table 1) easily qualifies on the first of these criteria, and with 1% of European Dunlin and Grey Plover in winter, it qualifies twice on the second.

The Gwent shore is also important on a more local basis in winter. In the case of Dunlin and Grey Plover the Gwent birds represent about 40% and 50% respectively of the Welsh totals, while numbers of Knot in December 1973/74 exceptionally accounted for almost 90% of the Welsh total (40–50% would be a more usual proportion). In spring, the Gwent coast assumes great national importance for passage waders, with, in May, about 8% of the Dunlin and 9% of the Whimbrel passing through Britain. Preliminary data suggest that in May 1976 Gwent held an unprecedented 30% or more of British Whimbrel.

In the case of ducks, the agreed criteria for international importance of a site are that it should support a total of at least 10,000 birds or at least 1% of the N.W. European total for any one species. The Gwent coast falls far short of international importance on either of these criteria, although the Severn estuary as a whole (inclusive of Bridgwater Bay) qualifies for this status by virtue of (a) its total winter population of Wigeon, which exceeds 1% of the N.W. European population, and (b) the European White-fronted Geese at Slimbridge, which in winter represent between 3% and 5% of the total for N.W. Europe.

However, considered in a more local context, the ducks of the Gwent coast assume much greater significance. Firstly, it is the only site in the Severn estuary which regularly supports Scaup or Common Scoter and it also accounts for a large proportion of the Welsh estuarine populations of both species. Secondly, it supports as much as two-thirds of both the Severn and combined Welsh estuary populations of Shoveler.

Having determined the numbers of birds which make use of the Gwent coast, and having ascertained their national and international significance, it is appropriate that some consideration should be given to the effects that major development of the Severn estuary would have upon them.

Of the two most important current proposals, only one directly affects the Gwent coast, exclusive of the remainder of the Severn estuary. This is the *Airport Complex Scheme* (Hooker, 1970) which would involve the reclamation of the Portland Grounds, Usk Patch, Welsh Grounds, and Bedwin Sands, including Denny Island, in order to provide a site for an international airport, freshwater reservoir, docks complex and industrial development land. The full implications of this scheme for waders in Gwent have been extensively discussed elsewhere (Ferns, 1975) and here it will suffice to say that its implementation would destroy the intertidal feeding areas along the entire Uskmouth–Wye stretch (70% of the total inter-tidal feeding area within the county) which at present support about two-thirds of the county's winter wader population. Of duck species, only Shelduck would be seriously affected as other numerous species feed mainly on the Uskmouth–Peterstone stretch.

The other major proposal is the *Tidal Power Electricity Generating Station* (Shaw, 1974) which would, in essence, involve the building of a barrage, either from Lavernock Point to Brean Down, or from Aberthaw to Watchet. Only the latter barrage would include Bridgwater Bay.

The net result of this scheme, as outlined by Ferns (1975), would be the reduction of the tidal range within the barrage from the present 15 metres to about 5 metres. The " tides " within the barrage would not coincide with tides outside it, and would be restricted to the upper part of the existing range. This would result in the loss of about 80% of the existing inter-tidal mud, not only in Gwent, but throughout the Severn estuary.

The *Estuaries Enquiry* has revealed that the Severn estuary supports in the order of 100,000 to 125,000 waders (Table 1), which makes it the sixth most important site in Britain in terms of total numbers, and Lapwing, Ringed Plover and Grey Plover are all relatively more abundant in the Severn than in other parts of Britain. The effects of the barrage scheme upon populations of waders and surface-feeding ducks are difficult to predict with any accuracy, but they would inevitably be very detrimental.

Now that the first phase of the *Estuaries Enquiry* is complete and the data are being analysed, long-term plans have been drawn up for its continuation. There will, in future, be three full-scale counts scheduled for December, January and February of each winter, and it is hoped that adequate coverage of the most important areas will be achieved at other times of the year by unscheduled counts.

Hopefully, it will soon be possible to identify short-term fluctuations of numbers and to discern the more important long-term trends in estuarine populations. This sort of information will also make it easier to quantify the effects of environmental catastrophes (estuarine equivalents of the Torrey Canyon disaster).

During the course of the *Estuaries Enquiry*, winters in Britain have been exceptionally mild. In the event of a return to the colder winters characteristic of a long period preceding the 1970s, it is probable that there will be an increase in the Severn populations of both waders and ducks, as these are driven west by the relatively harsh conditions in eastern Britain.

Acknowledgements. The authors wish to thank all those observers who gave up so much time to make counts of the Gwent coast, and without whose information this report would not have been possible. We are particularly indebted to R. L. Adams, M. Bailey, R. Groves, T. G. Evans, G. Hill, S. N. G. Howell, J. S. Knapp, N. Lacey, W. Simpson, H. Skeeles, H. R. Thomas and C. Titcombe. We are also grateful to A. J. Prater, the National Organiser of the *Estuaries Enquiry*, for releasing unpublished data on waders in Gwent; to G. Atkinson-Willes and D. Salmon, of the Wildfowl Trust, for their most generous assistance in obtaining duck numbers for areas other than Gwent; and to Dr. P. N. Ferns for helpful criticism of the original manuscript.

CHAPTER 5

BREEDING DENSITIES OF COMMON SPECIES
by H. W. HAMAR

AS in other counties, the most systematically watched areas in Gwent are the major reservoirs and the coast. The attractions of these regions stem partly from the increased diversity of species which can be seen because of the proximity of both aquatic and terrestrial habitats, and partly from the relative ease with which aquatic birds can generally be seen and counted. By contrast, inland areas with a more limited range of species, but nevertheless more representative of the county as a whole, have received comparatively little systematic study. Areas in Gwent which have been given such attention are few, and appear to be limited to a total of four which have been studied as part of the British Trust for Ornithology's Common Birds Census.

The primary aim of this census was to investigate the status and numbers of birds — particularly the commoner ones — by means of breeding season censuses over a number of sample areas and repeated annually wherever possible. It was hoped that a comparison of such results would enable annual fluctuations in population level to be determined, as well as providing an opportunity to explore their probable causes and discover if there are any definite trends in numbers among certain species.

Table 1 lists the areas, or census plots, in Gwent together with the periods over which they were studied and the main habitats which they contain. The data obtained from the four plots has been of great value;

TABLE 1. *Common Birds Census plots in Gwent*

Name	Area (hectares)	Main habitat	Years studied	Main observer
Wern Farm	81*	Woodland, farmland	1963–71	H.W.Hamar
Upper Cwmbran	37	Scrub, deciduous woodland	1968–72	D. Bolton
St. Julians	21	Parkland	1973-74	K. Jones
Nash	69	Coastal levels	1975-76	M. Bailey

* Reduced to 67 hectares in 1969.

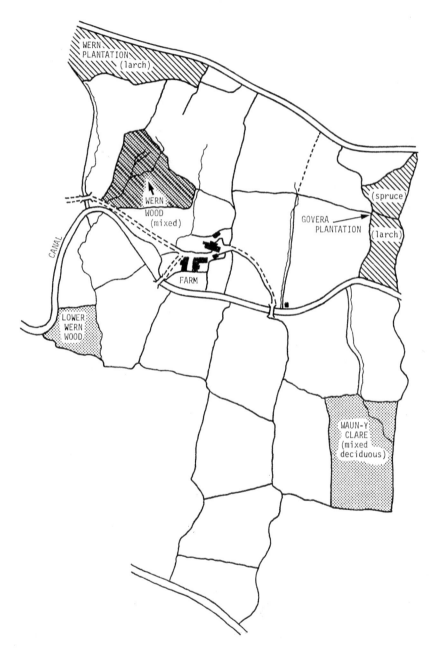

FIGURE 1. *Census area.*

32

in the cases of several species it has provided the only available information on their breeding densities and has been included in the appropriate section of chapter 8.

The remainder of the present chapter consists of a more detailed treatment of the results obtained at Wern Farm which is the longest-studied plot and was initially the largest of the plots.

The field work was done by members of the Gwent Ornithological Society usually during evenings, but occasionally during an early morning visit; about eight visits were made each breeding season. The breeding population was recorded using the standardised method devised by the B.T.O. Although an analysis of the results was carried out by observers at the close of each breeding season, the figures used in this account are taken from the analysis carried out by the Populations Section of the B.T.O.

Wern Farm is situated on an easterly facing slope at the southern extremity of the ridge which includes Mynydd Garn-wen and Mynydd Garn-clochdy. These hills lie at the eastern edge of the South Wales coalfield.

The highest land of the census area is over 180 m (600 ft.) and falls away steeply at first and gradually levels out to meet the main Pontypool–Abergavenny road at about 60 m (200 ft.), the vertical range being over 120 m (400 ft.). About 1½ km (nearly 1 mile) of the Monmouthshire–Brecon canal cuts through the centre of the whole area. There are five streams; three of them emerge from the hillside at about 150 m (500 ft.) and each cuts a quite deep trough in the lower area.

The census initially covered about 80 hectares (200 acres), some of this being woodland outside the farm boundary. In 1969 a large plot of mixed deciduous trees known as Cwmwdy Wood was felled to make way for the construction of a pharmaceutical factory. Two adjoining fields were also lost to the census area when the factory perimeter fence was erected, leaving a total of about 57 hectares (142 acres) of open farmland — a substantial area being used for pasture, the remainder chiefly for hay and cereals, leaving 15 hectares (38 acres) of woodland. At all times, however, the proportion of woodland has been almost one quarter of the total area, which is twice the figure for the county as a whole. This high proportion of woodland to open farmland seems to be not untypical of the whole eastern slope of the ridge. The fields on the higher slopes are divided by fences while those east of the canal are divided by hedges. A number of mature oaks grow in line with the hedges and fences.

A map of Wern Farm is shown in Figure 1 and brief descriptions of some of the most important habitats are given below:

1. Wern Plantation, situated above the 150 m (500 ft.) level is planted with larch with a peripheral belt of mostly hazel, hawthorn and holly and is an area favoured by Willow Warbler and Chiffchaff. Tree Pipit, Yellow-hammer and Redstart are rarely found below this altitude.

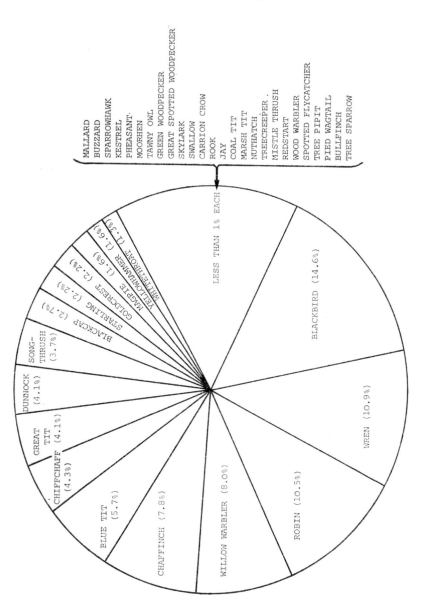

MALLARD
BUZZARD
SPARROWHAWK
KESTREL
PHEASANT.
MOORHEN
TAWNY OWL
GREEN WOODPECKER
GREAT SPOTTED WOODPECKER
SKYLARK
SWALLOW
CARRION CROW
ROOK
JAY
COAL TIT
MARSH TIT
NUTHATCH
TREECREEPER.
MISTLE THRUSH
REDSTART
WOOD WARBLER
SPOTTED FLYCATCHER
TREE PIPIT
PIED WAGTAIL
BULLFINCH
TREE SPARROW

LESS THAN 1% EACH

BLACKBIRD (14.6%)

WREN (10.9%)

ROBIN (10.5%)

WILLOW WARBLER (8.0%)

CHAFFINCH (7.8%)

BLUE TIT (5.7%)

CHIFFCHAFF (4.3%)

GREAT TIT (4.1%)

DUNNOCK (4.1%)

SONG-THRUSH (3.7%)

BLACKCAP (2.7%)

STARLING (2.2%)

GOLDCREST (2.2%)

MAGPIE (1.6%)

YELLOWHAMMER (1.6%)

WHITETHROAT (1.3%)

FIGURE 2. *Percentage composition of the breeding bird community of Wern Farm and adjoining woodland.*

2. Govera Plantation, with spruce at the lower altitude and larch on the higher ground. Again, Willow Warbler and Chiffchaff are the principal breeders, together with Goldcrest.

3. Wern Wood, a mixed deciduous plot of mainly birch, poplar and ash with a few firs and alder near the streams and sparse ground flora. Wood Warbler and Green Woodpecker nest here.

4. Lower Wern Wood, mainly poplar, ash, birch, hazel and holly with a fair ground cover of bracken and bramble. Typical woodland species are recorded here.

5. Waun-y-Clare, ash, oak, elm, alder, elder and hazel. The floor is densely covered with bramble and bracken. Spotted Flycatcher and Blackcap are usually recorded.

6. Canal. Lined for much of the way with alders, some ivy clad trunks offer nesting sites for Spotted Flycatcher. The tow-path side is mostly hedged. Moorhen are regular breeders and one pair of Mallard often occurs.

7. Hedgerows and streams. Blackbird, Robin, Dunnock and Wren are the commonest species.

The bird community of this farm is formed chiefly by woodland and hedgerow song bird species with a much weaker representation of field species. The relative proportions of all breeding birds present are shown in Figure 2, and the actual population densities for the sixteen most numerous species are shown in Table 2. All these figures represent averages for 1969–71, the period following the reduction of the census area.

The adverse effects of the hard winter months of December 1962 and January–February 1963 (the most prolonged cold spell since 1740) were quite pronounced according to comparisons based on census work elsewhere. Our first census of breeding birds took place in 1963 and there were exceptionally low counts of some resident birds, particularly Blackbird and Wren. Both these species, however, made a remarkable recovery from 1963 to 1965: Blackbird from 17 pairs to 40 pairs and Wren from six pairs to 19 pairs. A comparison of these figures with Table 2 indicates a complete recovery for both these species in only two years. Goldcrests were not recorded in 1963 but since that date have averaged 3.7 pairs per season.

Since 1965 several of our summer visitors, for example Whitethroat, Willow Warbler and Chiffchaff, have suffered an abnormally high mortality in their winter quarters. The reasons for this are not clearly understood but are probably connected with droughts which have occurred in lands south of the Sahara (Winstanley et al., 1973). Even taking into account the reduction of the census area in 1969, this national trend is well reflected in the Wern Farm totals. Figure 3 shows the decline of these species from 1965 to 1971: Whitethroat from 8 pairs to 4 pairs, Willow Warbler from 26 pairs to 8 pairs and Chiffchaff from 18 pairs to 6 pairs.

TABLE 2. *Bird community at Wern Farm and adjoining woodland 1969–71*

	Average Number of Pairs on 180 acres	Dominance % of Community	Average Number of Pairs on 100 acres	Average Number of Pairs on 1 km²
Blackbird	25.0	14·6	13·9	34·3
Wren	18·7	10·9	10·4	25·7
Robin	18.0	10·5	10·0	24·7
Willow Warbler	13·7	8·0	7·6	18·8
Chaffinch	13·3	7·8	7·4	18·3
Blue Tit	9·7	5·7	5·4	13·3
Chiffchaff	7·3	4·3	4·1	10·0
Great Tit	7·0	4·1	3·9	9·6
Dunnock	7·0	4·1	3·9	9·6
Song Thrush	6·3	3·7	3·5	8·7
Blackcap	4·7	2·7	2·6	6·5
Goldcrest	3·7	2·2	2·1	5·1
Starling	3·7	2·2	2·1	5·1
Magpie	2·7	1·6	1·5	3·7
Yellowhammer	2·7	1·6	1·5	3·7
Whitethroat	2·3	1·3	1·3	3·2

The figures in columns 3 and 4 are obtained from those in column 1 by multiplying by conversion factors; it is standard B.T.O. practice to present population density data in terms of these standard areas to facilitate comparison with other census plots.

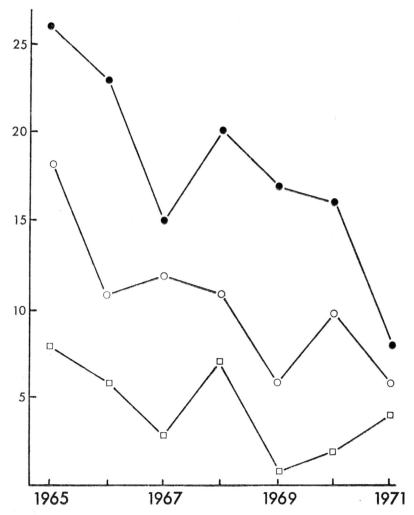

FIGURE 3. *The decline of summer visitors at Wern Farm from 1965 to 1971.* Total numbers of three species are indicated: ●—● = Willow Warbler; O—O = Chiffchaff □—□ = Whitethroat.

Figure 4 shows the relation between rainfall for the months of March, April and May, and the total number of breeding pairs of summer visitors. The close association between high breeding totals and low rainfall, and vice versa, is quite remarkable, but it is not clear whether the graph actually illustrates the decline of breeding pairs during wet seasons, or some other factor such as a corresponding suppression of song resulting in low counts.

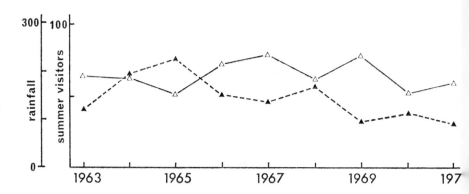

FIGURE 4. *Breeding summer visitors and rainfall at Wern Farm from 1963 to 1971.* ▲- - -▲ = total number of breeding summer visitors. △ — △ = total rainfall (mm) during the months March to May.

Keri Williams *Plate* 3. NIGHTJAR WITH YOUNG. Only the males have the white spots on the three outer primaries and the outer tail feathers.

Keri Williams   *Plate 4.* FEMALE BUZZARD WITH YOUNG.   The primary, secondary and tail feathers of the bird shown are very worn owing to continual abrasion on the nest.

CHAPTER 6

NESTBOX COLONIES

by P. F. J. Playford

THE exploitation of mature, deciduous woodland for timber and its clearance to allow house building, industrial expansion and the modernisation of farming methods, must eventually take their toll of many of our hole-nesting birds. Nestbox schemes in less mature woodlands help to counteract these trends by increasing the availability of nest-holes for some of our woodland species. The following account indicates the value of nest-boxes and summarises the breeding success and other results of interest from the Gwent colonies. It also gives some advice for the setting up of new colonies which is based largely upon my own experience in Gwent.

THE VALUE OF NESTBOX COLONIES

For many years it has been realised that in suitable areas of woodland, parks and gardens, devoid of natural holes, the erection of nestboxes provides nest-sites for many hole-nesting species. Today there are many types of nestbox available which enhance the garden and stimulate an interest in birds and their habits among casual birdwatchers and those who, for many reasons, are unable to participate more fully in the study of our avifauna.

For the serious ornithologist and ringer, nestboxes are a valuable source of information in the study of tit and flycatcher populations, their nesting materials, egg production, clutch sizes and young. Ringing of the nestlings is of particular value because their age is known with absolute certainty and their fledging success and subsequent mortality can often be determined. An opportunity is also provided to collect the fleas and parasites which are common to most nests. Thus nestboxes can provide pleasure in the opportunity for close-up observation of a family of birds, a means for scientific study and a valuable contribution to conservation.

NESTBOX COLONIES IN GWENT

Since 1967 there have been around seven nestbox colonies established in Gwent, containing a total of over 250 boxes and currently, new colonies are being set up in suitable areas of woodland whenever possible. It was unfortunate that some of the earlier colonies set up by members of the Monmouthshire Ornithological Society had to be abandoned because of human interference and predation, which is by far the most serious threat to nestboxes. As a result, valuable sites in the northern part of the county were lost.

One particular reason for establishing nestbox colonies in Gwent was to try to increase one of the rarer species of woodland bird, namely, the Pied Flycatcher, a migrant breeder from Africa which generally arrives during the last week of April or the first week of May. In Gwent, Pied Flycatchers were first reported at Caerleon in 1899; however, the first breeding record that I can find was not until 1923 at Abergavenny (Ingram and Salmon, 1939). The species is still not well established in our area, most probably because Gwent is on the fringe of its breeding range. Also, although there are many excellent small areas of mixed deciduous woodland in Gwent, we have very few large oakwoods with suitable ground cover above the 120 m (400 ft.) contour line, which is the type of habitat that Pied Flycatchers seem to prefer and which provides them with the necessary food requirements for themselves and their young. There may well be other reasons also.

In a large proportion of our woods alder is the dominant or co-dominant species of tree. Although this type of woodland is occupied in other parts of Britain, it does not seem to be favoured by Pied Fly-catchers in Gwent. The Gwent birds appear to have a requirement for woods with a high proportion of oaks. It is also significant that Pied Flycatchers are amongst the later migrants to arrive in our woodlands — at a time when natural nest holes are at a premium — which means that many birds will be forced to move on.

One would expect that the provision of nestboxes would help to overcome this problem and thus lead to an overall increase in Pied Flycatcher numbers in our area. While such an increase undoubtedly occurred in the early years after the establishment of the colonies, numbers have now been fairly stable for eight years and are clearly limited by other factors. These presumably include the extent of suitable woodland available, and the minimum territory size which a pair of breeding Pied Flycatchers will tolerate. My records show that the population in the north of the county was possibly at its best in 1970–71 (see Figure 1), prior to the inclement weather of May and June in 1971, when the mortality recorded in two of the colony populations of Pied Fly-catchers was about 16% of the adults and 95% of the fledglings, and may in fact have been higher. Blue and Great Tit populations also suffered heavy losses at this time (Playford, 1972).

Although increasing numbers of boxes by the formation of new colonies in suitable areas of woodland may contribute to the bird popula-tion as a whole, it is still far too early to say whether any other species has shown a significant increase in numbers as a result.

The annual totals of Pied Flycatchers, Blue Tits and Great Tits which have bred in the Gwent colonies, together with their breeding success is shown in Figures 1 and 2. Small numbers of Marsh Tits (up to four pairs annually) and Nuthatches (up to three pairs annually) also bred successfully in the colonies but are not illustrated.

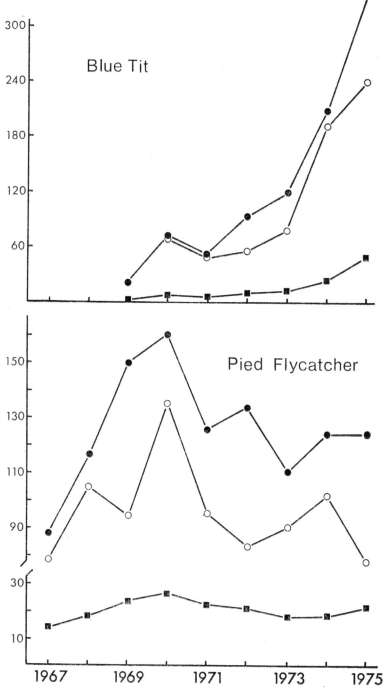

FIGURE 1. Numbers of Blue Tits and Pied Flycatchers breeding in nestbox colonies in Gwent from 1967 to 1975. ▦—▦ = number of breeding pairs; ●—● = number of eggs laid; O—O = number of young hatched.

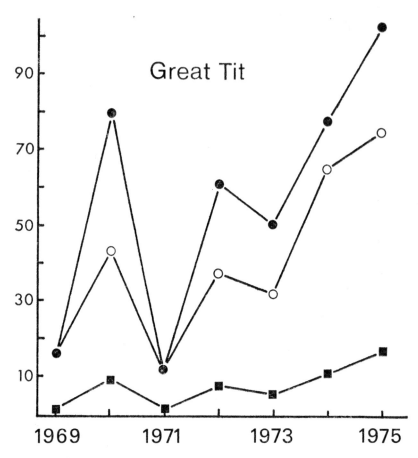

FIGURE 2. Numbers of Great Tits breeding in nestbox colonies in Gwent from 1969 to 1975. ■—■ = number of breeding pairs; ●—● = number of eggs laid; O—O = number of young hatched.

SOME INTERESTING OBSERVATIONS

Nestboxes help us to study population levels and fledging success, since many of the ringed birds return to the colony to breed year after year, some with their offspring. Birds ringed as nestlings in boxes can provide us with information on their subsequent dispersal as they are sometimes retrapped in different colonies. This may in part be due to changes of mate, for few birds pair for life; I have only found one pair of Pied Flycatchers which had the same partners for two consecutive years.

Polygyny (one male paired with more than one female) is not rare amongst Pied Flycatchers, and there is a variation from year to year in the territory held by the male when there is more than one breeding female. This may be related to the number of males present in a colony in a particular year. In 1976 there was polygyny in all the colonies, whereas in previous years it had occurred in only one or two.

When polygyny does occur, the brood sizes are inclined to be smaller, and my observations over many years have shown a marked difference in the size of the young in two different broods which hatched at the same time: the male seems to favour one brood until it has reached a satisfactory stage of growth before concentrating on the other brood. For example, in one colony in 1974, a male was trapped in box 12 which had a brood of six well feathered young. In box 27 (200 m away) there was another brood of five very small young; both broods had in fact hatched on the same day. After an absence of several days, a male was trapped in box 27, and was found to be the same male from box 12. The first brood, now fully fledged, was ready to leave the nest, but the other brood was still not fully fledged five days later.

Many broods fail altogether when the male deserts the female, or dies. I have observed this on a number of occasions in different colonies, and it most often occurs during the female's first breeding year. When there is an abundance of food, or the females are more mature, broods often survive without the help of the male.

It is generally asserted that male Pied Flycatchers are more loyal to the colony, but in Gwent I have found the females to be equally faithful. In fact, one female ringed as an adult in 1970 returned to the colony for six consecutive years, often using the same nestbox. In 1975 she returned with her daughter (now in her second year), having completed at least six migrations to Africa and back!

Other species are just as interesting. I can recall one occasion when one of a brood of nine Blue Tits ringed in a colony, was retrapped when feeding in my garden in January, eight months later and 16 km from where it was first ringed — very strange that it should have over-wintered in the garden of the person who ringed it!

Blue Tits are usually fairly sedentary; of the birds ringed in the colonies, those which have been retrapped or found dead have generally been within a radius of 32 km from the place where they were hatched. However, one adult Blue Tit retrapped in the area had been ringed at Devizes (Wilts.), 80 km away. Ringing in the area has also proved that some Blue Tits and Coal Tits have survived for as long as three years, quite a long period of time considering that a large proportion of Blue Tits die within the first year of their lives.

Great Tits breed regularly in the colonies which are adjacent to agricultural land. At one colony the adjacent land ceased to be worked as farmland three years ago and from this time Great Tits have ceased to breed in the colony. The fact that Great Tit populations in other colonies have remained comparatively stable suggests that the proximity of agricultural land may be important to this species.

Many other hole-nesting species are also interesting to watch. Take the Nuthatch, the " nut-hacker," for instance; it is well known that this species will block up a nest-hole until it is the right size to keep out predators and other intruders. The birds using nestboxes also completely seal the lid inside and outside with a thick layer of mud, which prevents it from opening.

Species such as the Marsh Tit and the Coal Tit frequently use nestboxes, but in recent years there seems to have been a decline in the number of Coal Tits present in the colonies, with no records of their breeding in nestboxes for four years.

When Wrens use a nestbox, they generally construct a conventional " domed " nest within it. Several pairs have reared their young in this type of nest in the last few years, and year by year the number of boxes used for this purpose has increased. The reason for this change is not known at present.

SOME GUIDANCE ON THE ESTABLISHMENT OF NEW COLONIES

Construction of nestboxes. There are many types of nestbox available to the general public. These can be obtained from garden centres, or preferably from the Royal Society for the Protection of Birds. Unfortunately, some have only aesthetic value and meet few of the requirements of our breeding woodland species. Because of this, many people prefer to build their own nestboxes and detailed plans for construction can be found in Flegg and Glue (1971).

However, it is worth mentioning here that the open-front boxes recommended for the Robin are all too frequently predated and I have found it safer to construct a box with a slot about 4 cm. (1½ in.) wide in the upper section of the front. Both Robin and Great Tit will favour this type of box.

Siting of nestboxes. There are extensive mixed deciduous woodlands in Gwent; some cover large areas, others only a few hectares, and all support a wide variety of birds. However, when setting up a colony it must be borne in mind that fewer birds will occupy boxes in old mature woodland where there is already an abundance of natural nestholes. Therefore, boxes sited in less mature woodland are more likely to be used and as they provide additional nest sites, they help increase the bird population of the area.

The position of a nestbox is of the utmost importance. The height of the box should be appropriate to the prevailing circumstances; for example, if there is fear of interference from humans or cats, it should be erected at a reasonable height — say 4–6 m (12-20 ft.) above ground level, on an outbuilding or tree, or perhaps the side of a house. All aids to climbing up to the box should be removed. Predation by humans in nestbox colonies over the past few years has been very severe and is by far the worst problem birds have to face.

The direction of the box is also a point worthy of consideration. My observations over the last few years have shown that boxes with holes facing S.E. through S. to S.W. have been occupied more frequently than those with holes that are facing a northerly aspect (Playford, 1976). This conflicts with the conventional advice to site boxes so that they face N.E. The evidence I have obtained in this field of research is by no means conclusive, because many factors remain to be considered, and therefore I suggest that the main consideration should be to site the box so that some protection from the elements is assured.

If the boxes are to be sited in woodlands they should be concealed as much as possible, away from public footpaths etc., and as high as possible, but within reach of a small extension ladder so that the contents may be inspected and recorded.

The British Trust for Ornithology has a Nest Record Scheme in operation. All information on nests and nestboxes is required for the purpose of research. Upon request they will supply cards for reporting the contents of nests and the outcome of broods.

Species of tree. Particular species of bird generally show very little preference for particular species of tree, but some of my research into tree selection has shown that certain species of tree on which boxes have been erected show a higher occupation ratio than others. Table 1 shows the species of bird using nestboxes on a variety of trees. This relates only to the type of woodland at present used for nestbox colonies in Gwent.

Very few boxes erected on beech trees are ever occupied. This may be due to the fact that beech trees are inclined to be wet and cold, when water drains down the smooth bark. The results in Table 1 are by no means conclusive. They are a summary taken over a period of three years and involved three colonies of a similar nature with a total of 100 boxes.

Table 1. *Percentage occupation of nestboxes on particular tree species in Gwent woodlands.*

Species of tree	Alder	Oak	Ash	Birch	Beech	Hawthorn and others
Number of boxes on each tree	37	21	15	17	5	5
Species of bird	Percentage occupation of nestboxes					
Great Tit (24)	5·4	7·9	6·7	15·7	0	6·7
Blue Tit (42)	10·8	17·5	15·6	15·7	13·3	13·3
Marsh Tit (7)	0·9	1·6	2·2	5·9	0	6·7
Nuthatch (5)	2·7	1·6	0	0	6·7	0
Pied Flycatcher (61)	25·2	28·6	22·3	6·0	6·7	6·7
TOTAL	45·0	57·1	46·7	43·1	26·7	33·3

The percentage in this table is based on nestbox occupation over a period of three years, so that, for example, nestboxes on alders could have been occupied for a total of 3 x 37 = 111 times in all. Then the figure for Great Tit in this column (for example), is 5·4% of 111, which is 6; that is, Great Tits occupied nestboxes on alders six times in the three years.

The figures in brackets under each species represents the total number of pairs of the species involved in this analysis.

Visits to the box. Information on birds breeding in boxes is a valuable asset to ornithological societies and individual ornithologists interested in bird behaviour. Studies of this type require great caution on the part of the observer. Time your visits carefully! Do not visit the box too often. Breeding birds often desert the nest in the early stages of incubation. Once in six or seven days is sufficient to obtain the total number of eggs laid. Always flush the bird from the box if possible and never slam the lid shut if the bird is still on the nest — it could prove fatal for the adult bird and her young.

Remember that the birds' welfare must be of prime importance at all times. Be discreet — there are still a number of egg collectors about despite the fact that egg collecting is an offence under the Protection of Birds Act 1954–1967. In 1975 a total of 89 eggs was stolen from one Gwent colony alone. Observation of the birds using the nestbox can provide many hours of pleasure and interest, if the observer is well concealed and at a distance from the box.

One other point to be mentioned — never place food near to the nestbox during the breeding period. Peanuts and other titbits fed to young birds in the nest often kill them. It is also an invitation to predators such as rats and mice and the neighbours' cat.

In winter, nestboxes often provide a shelter and night roost for many species of bird. During the course of the year I have also found the following uninvited guests using our nestboxes; Bankvole, Dormouse, Long-eared Bat, Woodmouse, Bumble-Bees, Wasps — all have taken some advantage of artificial nest sites.

CONCLUSION

In this short chapter I have discussed the advantages of nestboxes to the woodland species that use them. May they long help to increase the numbers of our hole-nesting species, for in an age of concrete jungles and diminishing mature woodland our countryside will otherwise become much impoverished.

CHAPTER 7

MIGRATION

by P. N. FERNS

THERE are two dominant sets of geographical features which exert a strong influence on bird migration in the county. The first consists of the valleys of the Usk and Wye, which together with their tributaries, form natural routes from the Severn estuary into the hinterland of Wales for those species, which under certain conditions, migrate at low altitude. For example, a northward spring passage of Whimbrel, Redshank and Curlew is recorded at night during most years over Cwmbran and Abergavenny. On the other hand, Dunlin, Ringed Plover, Redshank and Sanderling have all been observed leaving Collister Pill during April or May towards the north, calling intensely and climbing to a height of several hundred metres. Similar daylight migration departures of Dunlin, Ringed Plover and Whimbrel have been observed towards the north-east. For these birds, the river valleys can be of little significance, except perhaps as aids to navigation. During the autumn, however, these same valleys serve as important channels for the southward movement of finches, thrushes, larks, pipits and wagtails.

The second important geographical feature in Gwent is the coastline. Coastal migration in spring is rather poorly developed, with movements of hirundines, Swifts, Turtle Doves and Starlings being most notable, but reaching maximum rates of only about a dozen or so per hour during April and May. These movements have been recorded in both directions, but the upchannel (north-easterly) one dominates.

The autumn coastal migration is much more well marked and consequently better documented, with peak rates of well over a thousand birds per hour recorded for Chaffinches, Linnets and Redwings. These records are sufficiently detailed to merit further discussion.

DIURNAL MIGRATION

The most productive coastal migration watches in the county are summarized in Table 1. It is clear from the table that movements in both directions are recorded, with one particular direction usually dominant in any one watch. The main passage commences towards the end of September, reaches its peak in October and continues on into November. Thereafter, cold weather movements may take place, but these are generally over a broad front and have only a small coasting component. Movements characteristically start at dawn, and are in full flow from about half an hour after sunrise until two or three hours later, when they peter out rapidly. Since the same diurnal pattern occurs at many sites, this suggests that birds stop migrating during the latter part of the day, perhaps spending the remaining daylight hours feeding. Flock size varies from a mere handful up to a thousand, with typical figures in the range 10–100. On one occasion (Hamar and Wilkinson, 1969) it was possible to estimate the speed of movement of Pied Wagtail flocks along the 10 km (6 mile) stretch between Undy and Goldcliff, at about 39 km/hour (24 m.p.h.). This in turn suggests that these migrants move of the order of 80–160 km (50 – 100 miles) per day.

The other notable feature of Table 1 is that, without exception, the dominant direction of the coasting movement is against the prevailing wind. This is in accordance with radar observations showing that birds generally cross the coast without deviation in a following wind, but in the presence of a headwind or adverse crosswind, prefer instead to proceed along the coastline in a way that most closely follows their intended direction of travel (Eastwood, 1967). Such behaviour may enable them to take advantage of whatever reduction in wind velocity the shore can provide. Since radar studies have also shown that the greatest amount of migration takes place in the presence of a following wind (Lack, 1963), this means that the heaviest coastal migration is often seen from the ground at a time when comparatively little overall migration is taking place. Local observers know well that the best conditions for a good coasting movement are fresh winds with cloud or rain, while light winds and clear skies mean that little will be seen. Under the latter conditions, a great deal of migration may be taking place, but it is likely to be at a considerable height and over a broad front.

Despite the marked dependence of migratory direction at ground level upon wind conditions, the more logical downchannel movement is still numerically the most important in Gwent in autumn. The average number of birds counted on the eight days of predominantly downchannel movements in Table 1 was 1,620, whereas on the four days of predominantly upchannel movement it was only 673. There is thus a bias of more than two to one in the south-westerly direction. In order to determine the significance of these movements it is necessary to examine migration records from adjacent parts of the Severn estuary and Bristol Channel. Fortunately, during the last few years there have been a number of co-ordinated autumn migration watches in the region, organised by N. T. Lacy and M. Sainsbury of the Bristol Ornithological Club, the results of which have been published in various issues of the B.O.C. Bird News. As with the Gwent data, these counts show more than just a simple pattern of movement, in fact there are a number of complex and sometimes apparently contradictory reverse migrations. An account of these movements along the southern shores of the estuary has already been published (Sainsbury, 1972) and it is planned to produce further accounts in due course. For present purposes, only the dominant direction of movement at each site has been considered, and then it has been necessary to make a number of simplifications. Firstly, all the species have been

TABLE 1. *Morning migration watches along the Gwent coast*

SPECIES	PETERSTONE WENTLOOGE				GOLDCLIFF					SUDBROOK			TOTALS	
	28/9/75	5/10/75	12/10/74	12/10/75	6/10/68	12/10/74	14/10/73	19/10/68	13/11/74	12/10/74	12/10/75	25/10/75	Down-channel	Up-channel
Stock Dove					1								1	
Wood Pigeon	43	90	3 *(1)*			*(3)*		550	20		*219*	226 *17*	226	236
Skylark		*5*		50	105	*1*	*10*				*10*		791	90
Swallow		*(24)*		*8*	*16*		2						18	14
House Martin									*1*					6
Blue Tit				5	6								6	18
Coal Tit				*18*							3 *13*			3
Mistle Thrush				*19*								3		62
Fieldfare							*1*	373	27				373	275
Redwing								3500	275				3500	
Blackbird					*1*				3			*7*	1	4
Meadow Pipit	874 *(45)*	700	8 *65*	19 *205*	820	29 *(12)*	100+	290	195	*18*	15	9	2740	607
Rock Pipit	13	17	15	20			37	3		31	23 *190*		3	80
Pied/White Wagtail					400		*100* *(95)*	26					502	434
Starling					83			90	*141*			*3*	173	
Greenfinch						2			62	29 *(6)*		*14*	2	105
Goldfinch	38	43	2	13	105	69 *16* *(14)*	91		200	22 *6*	*14*	120 *(12)*	399	340

50

Species	1	2	3	4	5	6	7	8	9	10	11	12	Total (down)	Total (up)
Redpoll	8												19	*19*
Bullfinch		12	9										2	
Chaffinch	32		9	41	102	12 (22)	7	1200	*10+*	15	2	2	1370	*313*
Yellowhammer					2	2	*14*		*144*	*17*	*41*	*73*	2	*16*
Brambling									*39*		*16*	*1*		*57*
Reed Bunting					160				*1*			*12*	160	*13*
Tree Sparrow														
TOTAL	1086	1193	244	592	3801	294	555	6084	1138	204	630	492	16,313	
Downchannel	1041	1164	178	129	3801	214	460	6084		128		348	13,087	
Upchannel		5	65	463		29			1138	70	630	132		2,992
Source	1	2	3	4	5	6	7	8	9	10	11	12		

Sources

1, 2, 4:— Dr. W. A. Venables (pers. comm.). 1:—Wind S.W. 2:—Wind S.W. 4:—Wind N.E.

3, 6, 10:— Bristol Ornithological Club. Bird News, October 1974, pp. 6—7. Wind W/N.W. force 2, visibility good.

5, 8:— Hamar and Wilkinson (1969). 5:—Wind S.W. light. 8:—Wind S.E. light.

7:— Bristol Ornithological Club. Bird News, November 1973, pp. 7—8. Wind E. force 4—5, light rain.

9:— Bristol Ornithological Club. Bird News, November 1974, pp. 7—8. Wind E/S.E. light, visibility poor.

11, 12:— Bristol Ornithological Club. Bird News, October 1975, pp. 7—9. 11:—Wind N.E. force 2, visibility excellent. 12:—Wind S. very light, fog patches. The directions of movement at Sudbrook have been slightly simplified.

Key — Downchannel movements are shown in light numerals and upchannel movements in italics. Movements in any other directions are in brackets.

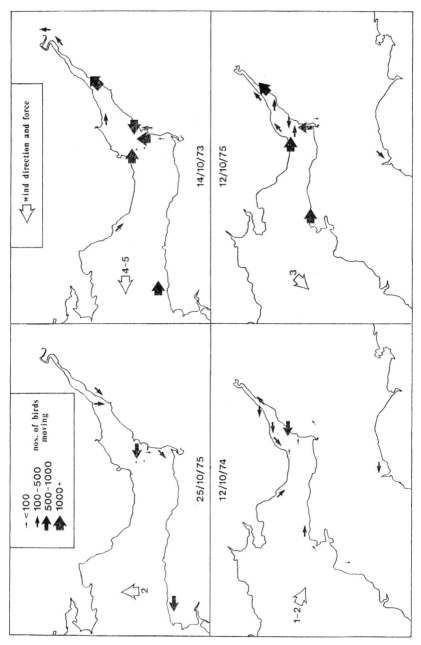

FIGURE 1. *Diurnal passerine migration in the Bristol Channel on four days.* Data mainly from Bristol Ornithological Club, Bird News; October 1973, 1974 and 1975.

lumped together and secondly, Starlings have had to be excluded because of the possibility of confusion between genuine migration and dawn dispersal from roosts. The resultant simplified pattern of movement for four contrasting days is shown in Figure 1. The significance of wind direction is once again immediately apparent. On 25th October 1975, there was a fairly clear cut southerly and westerly movement of birds out of the Bristol Channel against prevailing southerly winds. On 14th October 1973, there was an exceptionally heavy passage in the opposite direction. An average of 1,500 birds per observation point were seen on this occasion, compared with only 400–800 on the other three days. Furthermore, 66 % of these birds were Chaffinches, whereas this species normally constitutes only 30–45 % of all birds seen. 12th October 1974 was a day of light winds and complicated movements, to such an extent that only just over 50 % of the birds were moving in the directions shown, whereas on all the other days at least 80 % of birds were moving in the directions indicated. 12th October 1975 was another day of predominantly upchannel movement with Redwings rather more abundant than usual, forming 26 % of the total number of birds seen.

Co-ordinated watches, such as those shown in Figure 1, can provide a great deal of information about the effects of weather on migration, but more frequent observation is necessary to establish the dominant pattern of movement at any particular site. This dominant pattern for some of the more regularly watched areas is shown in Figure 2. The downchannel coasting in Gwent, at both Goldcliff (a) and Peterstone Wentlooge (b), is clear both from Table 1 and from sporadic records over a number of years. The situation at Sudbrook is more complex and has thus not been entered on the figure. The dominance of south-easterly coasting at Porthcawl (c) and easterly coasting at Lavernock Point (d) is well established (Heathcote, Griffin and Salmon, 1967; S. F. Young, pers. comm.). The direction of movement over Flat Holm and Steep Holm (e) is nearly always to the south or east (Heathcote, Griffin and Salmon, 1967; Chadwick, 1962; Steep Holm Gull Research Station Reports 1963, 1965, 1969). At Burnham-on-Sea (f), Holt (1950, 1960) recorded only southward movements, and this direction of travel is maintained by most birds at least as far south as Pawlett (g). The dominant movements described so far fit into a clear pattern of a funnelling towards Lavernock Point and a channel crossing via the comparatively short and convenient island route, as suggested by Morley (1972). The preferred direction of travel is thus towards the south, which is not surprising in autumn. However, not all observations fit into such a neat pattern. There has for example, been a dominant north-easterly component at New Passage (h) (N. T. Lacy, pers. comm.). This site is, however, at the neck of the natural funnel formed by the estuary and may thus receive the whole of whatever north-easterly stream may be passing along either coast, thus outweighing any downchannel movement, even on days when the latter direction dominates at other sites.

53

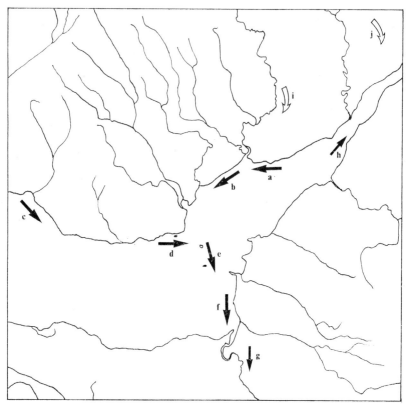

FIGURE 2. *Dominant direction of movement of diurnal migrants at well watched sites.*

The birds passing along the Gwent coast could originate from several sources. They may come from the north-east coast of England, being part of the south-westerly stream observed by Raines (1950) passing down the Trent valley, which could easily link up with the Severn valley as suggested by Holt (1950). Such a route need only be taken in adverse wind conditions of course. There is also a strong indication (Hamar and Wilkinson, 1969) of a passage down the Usk valley (i). Finally, Lack and Lack (1949) made specific mention of a southerly stream of diurnal migrants crossing the Forest of Dean (j) towards the Severn.

As to the destination of those birds continuing south along the river Parrett, it is clear that they could maintain their southerly course along the coast of Devon and achieve a channel crossing perhaps towards Brittany, or they could move south-eastwards and join the vast throng of migrants which pass south over Portland Bill (Clafton, 1976) on the shorter channel crossing to Normandy.

Keri Williams

Plate 5. DUNLIN. The commonest shore bird in Gwent. The bird shown above has almost completed its autumn moult but a few darker, summer plumage feathers can still be seen on its back.

Keri Williams   *Plate 6.*   GREENSHANK. This bird may occur at any sizeable stretch of water, particularly in ... have much whiter heads and breasts than the one shown here.

It is worth emphasising that the direction of migration in a species may depend very much on the particular subspecies or population which is involved. For example, in the case of the Meadow Pipit there is a local southward exodus of the British breeding population (*Anthus pratensis pratensis*), an eastward movement of the Icelandic race (*A.p.theresae*) and a westward movement of continental birds (also *A.p.pratensis*). (Heathcote, Griffin and Salmon, 1967).

THRUSHES

Since thrushes migrate both by day and night, dawn migration watches do not always provide a realistic appraisal of the movements which may be occurring. Some information about the arrival of local

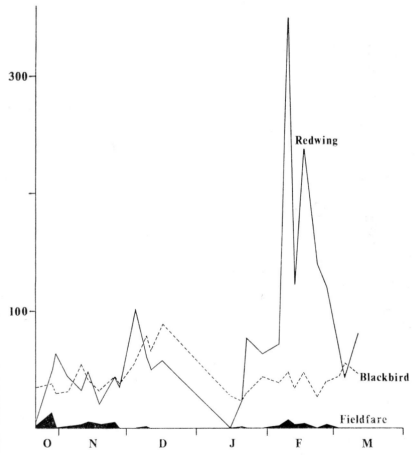

FIGURE 3. *Fluctuations in the numbers of thrushes on the Wentlooge Levels in 1975/6.*

birds is available from counts at approximately five day intervals on a 160 hectare (400 acre) plot of typical farmland in the Wentlooge Levels during the course of the 1975/6 winter (Hansford, 1976). The coastal lowlands of Gwent provide an important wintering area for several species and counts of three of them on this plot are shown in Figure 3. In the case of the Redwing there were small influxes in October and at the end of November, followed by a decline during the Christmas period and a massive influx following a cold spell with snow in February. Blackbird numbers show some evidence of an influx in late November followed by a departure in December, and a similar pattern occurs in the Song Thrush and Mistle Thrush, though these are not illustrated. Fieldfare numbers were exceptionally low in the 1975/6 winter, perhaps as a result of the almost complete failure of the haw crop.

The overall mean densities of these species per 100 hectares throughout the winter months were as follows — Redwing 48, Blackbird 27, Song Thrush 7, Mistle Thrush 3, Fieldfare 1. Because of the poor berry crop and the comparatively mild winter these do not necessarily provide a fair assessment of the importance of the coastal levels for these species, however. The Wentlooge and Caldicot Levels constitute between them about 14,000 hectares, and the above figures suggest a minimum wintering Redwing population of 7,000. The density in February 1976, on the other hand, suggests a peak population of about 30,000.

SEA BIRDS

It has been suggested that the Wash / Vale of Catmose / Vale of Evesham / Severn axis might form a convenient overland short cut for sea birds from the North Sea heading for the Western Approaches, and there is at least a little evidence to support this. Jones (1966) recorded an exceptional downchannel movement of 80 Arctic Skuas and five Pomarine Skuas past Lavernock Point in October 1963. There is also a small spring and autumn passage of terns along several nearby coasts (Davis, 1971; Rabbitts, 1971). Systematic sea-watches in Gwent could prove most valuable in gaining further information in this regard. The most productive weather conditions are likely to be westerly winds in autumn and easterlies in spring, for at such times migrants can be expected to be flying lower than normal.

Many records of sea birds in the inner Bristol Channel occur within a few days of south-westerly gales and thus consist of down-channel recovery movements of storm blown individuals. King and Perrett (1963) describe a particularly well-marked example of this, when on 13th February 1962, 490 Kittiwakes flew west past Minehead following severe gales the day before. It is becoming increasingly clear, however, that there are other types of movement involved as well. For example Rabbitts (1971) says of the Manx Shearwater " occurs with regularity in the upper reaches of the channel. Most are weather movements in anticyclonic conditions or in areas of low pressure .... when birds move up channel to avoid them. Occasionally they are seen to search for food." In the case of another species, the Kittiwake, there is evidence of a recent change in status (Rabbitts, 1972) with birds becoming increasingly common during fine weather in spring.

Manx Shearwater records along the coast of Gwent have increased during recent years, but this probably reflects greater coverage rather than any real change in status. These movements have occurred during a variety of weather conditions and thus require some explanation. All the sightings from local bird reports between 1970 and 1974 are summarized in Figure 4. While such records are by no means an unbiased sample of the real movements, they do illustrate several significant features. Despite great variation in observer coverage, the relative lack of penetration of this species into the Severn estuary proper is apparent. The inner channel movements are dominated by sightings in June and July, whereas April and August records are also common in Somerset and Gower. At these latter sites, many of the birds are breeding adults, associated with the nearby colonies on the Pembrokeshire islands and Lundy (Lockley, 1953 p.18). Why deeper penetration of the channel should occur in June and July is more difficult to determine. Even though feeding has occasionally been observed, suitable foods such as sardines and young herrings are scarce in the inner channel, and sprats do not arrive to spawn until the autumn (Lloyd, 1942). The period in question does correspond, however, with the large scale arrival of adult non-breeders at the Pembrokeshire colonies (Perrins, Harris and Britton, 1973). This is also the time of year when birds visit headlands and islands where there are no colonies (Penhallurick, 1969; Harris, 1972). June and July movements within the inner Bristol Channel could consist of such non-breeding birds. General exploratory flights could lead to the attempted colonisation of suitable areas in future seasons. Such an attempt presumably explains the presence of a fresh Manx Shearwater corpse, found on the ground at the Worms Head, Gower, on 23rd March 1974. This individual had enlarged testes, indicating that it may have been in breeding condition, and possibly occupied one of the many burrows on the island.

RINGING

The shortage of qualified ringers in even the most heavily populated industrial regions of South Wales has meant that comparatively little ringing has been done in Gwent. Complete records have never been kept and so it is difficult to arrive at an accurate total for the county as a whole, but by bringing together information from all the readily available sources, it emerges that at least 11,400 birds of 69 species have been ringed since 1960. The top ten most commonly ringed birds are shown in Table 2, together with the top ten for the whole of the British Isles up to the end of 1974 (Spencer and Hudson, 1976). It is immediately obvious that the Gwent figures are dominated by a handful of species to which a disproportionate amount of ringing effort has been devoted. This applies to

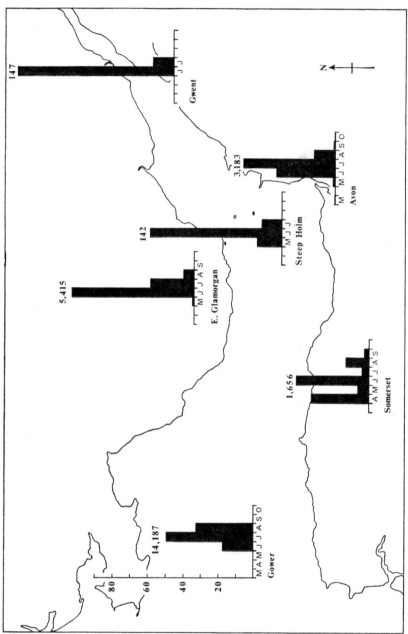

FIGURE 4. *Percentage of observations of Manx Shearwaters occurring in different months in different parts of the Bristol Channel from 1970 to 1974 inclusive*. The percentage scale is shown on the Gower histogram and the actual number of birds seen is shown at the top of the histogram for each site.

six out of the top seven, the single exception being the Greenfinch, a species which is being ringed in increasing numbers throughout Britain (it was in fact the second most frequently ringed bird in 1974, the latest single year for which national information is available).

In many ways it is encouraging to see so much of the ringing effort being channelled towards particular species. We shall see shortly how this approach has proved valuable in the study of Sand Martins and wading birds. However, there is also plenty of scope for a great deal of more general ringing. The possibilities of coastal sites such as Portskewett and Goldcliff during the migration period are well worth investigating.

TABLE 2. *Comparison of the most frequently ringed species in Gwent and the British Isles*

GWENT			BRITISH ISLES		
Species	No. Ringed	% of Total	Species	No. Ringed	% of Total
Sand Martin	4,488	39·4	Blackbird	680,058	7·2
Dunlin	2,591	22·7	Starling	635,645	6·7
Blue Tit	1,212	10·6	Blue Tit	566,140	6·0
Pied Flycatcher	846	7·4	Swallow	564,419	6·0
Great Tit	375	3·3	Sand Martin	490,683	5·2
Greenfinch	189	1·7	Greenfinch	449,539	4·8
Ringed Plover	139	1·2	House Sparrow	303,269	3·2
Blackbird	127	1·1	Song Thrush	228,290	3·1
Robin	123	1·1	Chaffinch	244,417	2·6
Sedge Warbler	113	1·0	Willow Warbler	240,156	2·5

One of the strongest influences on ringing in Gwent has been the presence, in the north of the county, of a number of woodlands supporting breeding populations of Pied Flycatchers. The ringing of nestlings from nestboxes in these areas is largely responsible for the high totals of Pied Flycatcher, Blue Tit and Great Tit in Table 2. These colonies and their history are discussed in detail in Chapter 6. However, it is worth emphasising at this point that none of the information about site consistency, mate fidelity, age of first breeding, polygyny, and so on, could have been collected without the aid of individually identifiable, durable marks of the sort that only the metal ring can provide.

Even the small amount of general ringing carried out in the area has yielded a number of spectacular recoveries, and any discussion of migration would be incomplete without mentioning some of them. One of the most interesting was an adult male Chaffinch, ringed at Gwehelog on 16th February 1972 and killed by traffic at Osnabrück in West Germany two months later. A Dunlin, ringed on its northward spring migration through the Severn estuary in May 1973 was controlled (i.e. caught alive and released) in November of the same year at the Banc d'Arguin in Mauritania. There have also been a number of foreign ringed birds recovered or controlled in Gwent, including a Danish Blackbird and Black-headed Gull, a German Water Rail, a Russian Common Gull, a Teal from Swedish Lapland and another from the Camargue, and a further Dunlin from Mauritania.

Two ringing studies will now be considered in further detail as examples of work carried out in Gwent which have yielded results of particular value and interest.

Sand Martin

In 1964, as part of the British Trust for Ornithology's Sand Martin Enquiry, a special effort was made in Gwent to ring as many birds of this species as possible. In addition, the nesting colonies along the length of the river Usk were surveyed to determine their size and number. Full details of the survey are given by Rogers and Gault (1968).

TABLE 3. *Movement of recaptured Sand Martins whose colonies had been destroyed during the preceding winter (after Rogers, 1970)*

Age When Ringed	Retrap Site		
	Nearest Undestroyed Colony	Further Away	Number
Adult ..	75%	25%	109
Juvenile ..	57%	43%	47

Most of the colonies were situated in the middle reaches of the river where the banks are formed of a particular type of fluviatile sediment, well-suited to the construction of secure nesting-holes. A total of 1,850 holes were counted (about 300 of these actually being in Brecknock), the largest single colony containing 210. One of the interesting features of this type of nesting habitat is that many holes have to be rebuilt each year, because whole sections of the bank are eroded away during the spates which occur after storms in winter, or occasionally during the breeding season (Sarson, 1969).

Between 1964 and 1967, 4,488 Sand Martins were ringed at the Usk and Afon Lwyd colonies. On average, 32% of the colonies worked in any one breeding season had completely disappeared by the next, the birds from such colonies being forced to nest at new sites. Ringed birds from these old colonies were often caught at their new homes in the succeeding season and the distribution of such retraps is shown in Table 3. When these movements are compared with those of birds from colonies which remained intact (Table 4) it can be seen that 90% of adults return to the same or nearest colony when both are available, and 75% move to the nearest when the original is destroyed. This indicates a very high degree of colony specificity. The actual percentage of ringed birds which were recaptured in the year immediately following ringing, averaged 8.4. This may appear low but it is close to values obtained for other hirundines, e.g. Chapman (1955).

All the information on the Usk colonies has been taken from the papers of Rogers and Gault (1968) and Rogers (1970), their work being

TABLE 4. *Movement of recaptured Sand Martins whose original colonies remained intact (after Rogers, 1970)*

Age When Ringed	Retrap Site			
	Same Colony	Nearest Colony	Further Away	Number
Adult ..	63%	26%	11%	140
Juvenile ..	31%	17%	52%	36

all the more valuable because the results of the national Sand Martin Enquiry have yet to be published. Movements in and out of the county (Table 5) do not show the usual pattern of decreasing numbers of recoveries (strictly, recoveries and controls) with increasing distance from the ringing (or recapture) site. Instead they fall into two main groups. The first occurs along a coastal strip from Norfolk to Hampshire and represents 68% of all recoveries. Of the birds in these areas, nearly 80% were caught at roosts in the autumn. It is characteristic of this species, as with swallows, that during the autumn migration period, adults and juveniles utilise a number of large roosts in the southern part of Britain. The very large number of recoveries from Sussex is the result of intensive ringing at one such roost near Chichester, which holds a peak number of about 30,000 birds (Mead, 1974). A similar roost in Norfolk holds up to a million. A smaller cluster of recoveries, representing 16% of the total, occurs in Radnor, Brecknock and Hereford. Since 80% of these birds were juveniles, caught at both roosts and breeding colonies they may simply be the result of dispersal of young birds in search of breeding sites for use in subsequent seasons. Tables 3 and 4 show clearly that juveniles tend to move much further than adults.

61

TABLE 5. *Movement of Sand Martins into and out of Gwent up to 1966. Old counties are referred to since these are still used for ringing purposes (after Rogers and Gault, 1968)*

Site of Ringing or Recovery	Number of Birds
Sussex	43
Kent	10
Brecknock	6
Radnor	6
Norfolk	5
Essex	4
France	4
Hampshire	4
Hereford	3
Gloucester	2
Middlesex	2
Somerset	2
Warwickshire	2
Worcester	2
Derbyshire	1
Oxfordshire	1
Shropshire	1
Spain	1
Stafford	1
Wiltshire	1

Wading Birds

Since 1972, the wading birds of the Gwent foreshore have been the subject of intensive study and ringing effort by members of the Celtic Wader Research Group. Cannon-nets have been used to capture birds on high tide roosts, notably at Collister Pill and Rumney Great Wharf (although the latter roost is in South Glamorgan, birds from it feed in Gwent). So far most of the effort has been concentrated in the spring and 2,834 birds have been captured up to May 1976, with Dunlin being the dominant species. 35 of these birds already carried rings from elsewhere and a further 12 have gone on to be recovered or controlled later. Dunlin recaptured in Gwent have carried rings from France, Holland, Denmark, East Germany, Sweden, Norway, Iceland and Mauritania. A complete list of recoveries and controls is given in Green (1976).

The age, sex, weight, wing and bill measurements of all trapped birds have been recorded as fully as possible, for this kind of information enables them to be assigned to particular subspecies or populations breeding in particular areas. The Gwent samples are quite small and the analyses are therefore not complete, but it is worth briefly examining one aspect of these measurements, namely the weights, and making some tentative comparisons with samples obtained elsewhere in the country.

In the case of Dunlin, spring migration weights show considerable variation depending on the subspecies being considered and the amount of premigratory fat being deposited. A sample of 112 birds caught in Gwent in March 1973 had a mean weight with one standard deviation of 49.6 ± 3.5g, yet only a few weeks later, the many samples caught in April and May had mean weights between 58 and 72g, with an occasional individual bird weighing as much as 91g. This illustrates how rapidly these birds are able to build up their premigratory fat reserves, which in some cases amounts to as much as 40g, and underlines the significance of the Severn estuary as a " fuelling " area in spring.

Midwinter weights are generally a little higher than those of late winter (such as the March sample). Unfortunately, there are no midwinter weights available for Gwent, but samples from other regions along the northern shores of the Bristol Channel had weights as follows.

Swansea Bay, adults and juveniles, December and January 1964 and 1965,

> 52.9 ± 4.3g   (48 birds)

Angle Bay, Pembrokeshire, 22nd January 1972,
> 50.5 ± 4.0g   (152 adults)
> 47.3 ± 3.2g   (21 juveniles)

Despite the diverse origins of these samples, they enable the following conclusions to be reached. Firstly, as reported from other wintering areas, juveniles are somewhat lighter than adults. Secondly, the difference between midwinter and March weights is quite small. In fact, only in the Swansea Bay sample (details kindly supplied by C. M. Reynolds), which was obtained in the two winters (1963/4 and 1964/5) following the very severe season of 1962/3, was the difference appreciable. Dunlin on the Wash differ markedly (Minton, 1975) showing a clear rise to a peak weight in mid-December of about 56g, falling back to about 48g in mid-March. It thus appears that midwinter Dunlin from the Bristol Channel are about 10% lighter than those from the Wash.

The much smaller samples of Redshank and Turnstone show evidence of similar differentials. Six Redshank from Collister Pill in March 1973 had a weight of 139 ± 8g, while those from the Wash average about 143g at the same time of year (Minton, 1975), and those from the Upper Clyde estuary, 147g (Mackie, 1976). 23 Turnstone caught on Sully Island, South Glamorgan, in March 1972, weighed 107 ± 6g (smaller midwinter samples from Angle Bay are almost identical), whereas weights on the Wash average about 114g in March and 123g in midwinter (Minton 1975).

Throughout the winter months, weight change in waders is correlated with day length (Minton 1973; Evans and Smith, 1975). These changes in weight result directly from changes in the amount of fat carried (Prater, 1975). This fat serves as a food reserve if conditions make feeding impossible (as when the mud flats freeze), as well as having an insulative function. Since much milder conditions generally prevail on the western side of Britain, waders in the Severn estuary presumably do not need such large fat reserves and are therefore lighter in weight. It should be emphasized however, that a great deal more information needs to be collected from the Severn estuary before our knowledge of local waders begins to approach that of the Wash birds.

A chapter such as this has inevitably had to draw upon the collected observations of a large number of workers, and it is, unfortunately, impossible to mention all of them by name. I am particularly grateful to those who took part in the dawn migration watches and to N. T. Lacy for providing me with copies of the data, as well as commenting on a draft of this section, along with S. F. Young. W. E. Jones made some valuable comments on the section on sea birds. The work on wading birds would not have been possible without the kind co-operation of local land-owners and tenants and I would particularly like to thank Mr. W. H. Attewell, Mr. D. W. Price and Mr. H. W. Neal, together with all my colleagues in the Celtic Wader Research Group.

CHAPTER 8

SYSTEMATIC LIST

THE following list includes all species which have been reliably identified within Gwent up to 31st December 1975. It also includes records from areas which at the time were within the old county of Monmouthshire but which are not part of the new county of Gwent; such areas carry the subscript (Monmouthshire). A number of species whose occurrence is more doubtful is included in an appendix to the list. In the cases of some rarer species the entries in the main list include both definite and doubtful records; in such instances the doubtful records are enclosed in square brackets. For further details of particular records reference should be made to the annual reports of the Gwent (formerly Monmouthshire) Ornithological Society or to quoted sources.

Place names and their spellings are those used on the Ordnance Survey 1:50,000 sheets (First Series). A complete list of places referred to, together with their National Grid References (to four figures) is given on pages 147–148.

The order of species is that of the British Trust for Ornithology's " Species List of British and Irish Birds," B.T.O. Guide no. 13, 1971 and the nomenclature is that of The British Ornithologists' Union (1971).

Abbreviations used are:— $c = circa$ (about)

C.B.C. = Common Birds Census

1 BLACK-THROATED DIVER *Gavia arctica*

Three records only: one found dead in a garden in Newport on 5th February 1915; one, considered " almost certainly this species," seen at Ynysyfro Reservoir on 20th January 1962, and one seen at Llandegfedd Reservoir on several dates in late December 1975.

2 GREAT NORTHERN DIVER *Gavia immer*

Rare winter visitor. Of the eleven records up to the end of 1975, six are of birds at Llandegfedd Reservoir from 1973 to 1975: two were seen on 3rd February 1974 and single birds on 14th November 1973, 2nd–3rd March, 15th–16th November and 29th December 1974, and, probably the same bird, on 12th January 1975. The remaining records are more varied, comprising: one found dead at Sor Brook, Caerleon, in March 1929; one at Blackwood in March 1931; an undated, but pre-1939, record of one shot at Llanbadoc; one at Ynysyfro Reservoir in October 1938 and one at Wentwood Reservoir in January 1967.

4 RED-THROATED DIVER *Gavia stellata*

The only record is of an adult in winter plumage, found dead at Newport Docks on 16th April 1964; this is surprising since the species is a regular visitor to coastal waters in southern Britain.

5 GREAT CRESTED GREBE *Podiceps cristatus*

Mainly a passage migrant and winter visitor in moderate numbers; rarely breeds, though small numbers remain through the summer. Most records in recent years are from Llandegfedd Reservoir, where birds have been seen through most of each year from 1964 to 1968 and throughout each year since then, the overall average population during the years 1969 to 1974 being six birds. Numbers usually remain fairly stable at about this level during the winter months, followed by a peak in April or May, typically of about 12 birds but occasionally as high as 26. A drop to low numbers (rarely more than two) during the summer months is often followed by a second, smaller, peak of up to about ten birds in early autumn.

The species is also regularly seen on Wentwood and Ynysyfro Reservoirs, St. Pierre Lake and also at Garnlydan Reservoir and nearby smaller waters on the high ground around Ebbw Vale; occasionally also on other inland waters but rarely on the coast. Records from these waters reflect seasonal variations similar to those at Llandegfedd, but in much smaller numbers.

There are only three definite breeding records: at St. Pierre Lake in 1971 and 1972 and at Llandegfedd in 1972. Owing to disturbance during the summer months, however, neither site is really suitable for this species.

7 SLAVONIAN GREBE *Podiceps auritus*

Rare winter visitor. There is only one record before 1970, of a female shot at Marshfield in the 1890s and sent to the National Museum of Wales (Ingram and Salmon, 1939). All recent records except two are from Llandegfedd Reservoir, where two were seen on 5th January 1970, with one on four other dates in January and February; one again on 24th October 1971, three on 3rd December 1974, and single birds on 25th January and 30th December 1975. The other records are from Ynysyfro Reservoir, where one stayed from mid-January to 10th March 1972, and from Wentwood Reservoir where one was seen on 16th and 30th December 1975.

8 BLACK-NECKED GREBE *Podiceps nigricollis*

Scarce passage migrant and winter visitor. Most of the records are of birds at Llandegfedd Reservoir, where from one to three birds have been seen on ten occasions over the years 1965 and 1968–71. Of these records, five are in the months December–February, four in the months August–October and one in April. Of the remaining four records, two are from Ynysyfro Reservoir; one shot on 6th September 1923 and one seen on 8th February 1970. The other two are of birds on the river Usk; one at Llanbadoc on 6th March 1948 and one at Newbridge-on-Usk on 25th February 1968.

9 LITTLE GREBE *Tachybaptus ruficollis*

Winter visitor and passage migrant in moderate numbers; rarely breeds. Although formerly described as a regular breeder on suitable waters throughout the county (Humphreys, 1963), there have been only three definite breeding records since 1965: at Undy Pool in 1966, Skenfrith in 1969 and Llanfoist in 1970. Most of the records in the years 1965 to 1974 are in the months November to March, with a few from August and into May, and none (apart from the breeding records) in June or July. The species is most frequently seen on the river Usk, mainly around Abergavenny, but also at various sites as far downstream as Newbridge-on-Usk, and at Llandegfedd Reservoir. Records are less regular, though still fairly frequent, from Magor–Undy, Ynysyfro, Garnlydan and Wentwood Reservoirs, and also from the reens at Peterstone Wentlooge, with occasional sightings elsewhere. In many cases birds are seen in ones and twos, though up to six together are not uncommon; a record of ten together at Llanwenarth in January 1972 is exceptional.

12 LEACH'S PETREL *Oceanodroma leucorrhoa*

Rare visitor with five records, all before 1953, and all of single birds. One, now in the Newport Museum, was shot at Llantarnam prior to 1937, and the remains of a specimen were found near Rhymney on 28th December 1948. Following the considerable " wreck " of this species in October 1952, corpses were discovered at Newport on 29th October, Peterstone Wentlooge on 30th November and Chepstow early in 1953.

14 STORM PETREL *Hydrobates pelagicus*

Two records only. One bird was found alive near Pontypool on 15th October 1963, but it died later and is now in Newport Museum. The other record is of a single bird found dead at Chepstow on 14th November 1964. Neither of the smaller species of petrel has yet been sighted offshore in the county.

16 MANX SHEARWATER *Puffinus puffinus*

Occasional juveniles from the Bristol Channel colonies are wrecked after autumn gales and there is also a regular movement in the channel. Over the years, fourteen recently fledged Manx Shearwaters have been found inland after gales — all in the short period 3rd to 21st September. Of these, three had been ringed on Skokholm only four, six and fifteen days earlier and so were probably on their first flights when caught in adverse weather conditions. They were found at a variety of places, including Llandenny, Monmouth, Llanbadoc and Nantyderry, but most were near the coast, e.g. one at Uskmouth, and several at the Llanwern steel works. Some of these birds died, but others recovered and flew strongly when released after a few days in captivity. The maximum number wrecked in any one year was four in September 1966, when there were also two oiled birds found in the same period at Magor and Monmouth.

In the last three years a small movement has been noted in the channel in midsummer, similar to that observed at Lavernock Point (S. Glamorgan) and Brean Down (Somerset). About 17 flew down-channel at Peterstone Wentlooge on 5th July 1973 about one mile offshore at high tide. 130 were flying back and forth, offshore from Undy at high tide on 23rd June 1974. 140 moved upchannel off Peterstone during the 90 minutes before high tide on 27th June 1975. The latter birds were mostly in small groups of less than 20, though the largest consisted of 72. A further 20 flew upchannel on the evening tide. The period of the main Bristol Channel movement of Manx Shearwaters (late June and early July) coincides with the arrival at Skokholm of large numbers of non-breeding adults (mean age about three years). It thus seems quite likely that these movements consist of non-breeding birds and it is just possible that they are undergoing some kind of prospecting for future breeding sites.

26 **FULMAR** *Fulmarus glacialis*

Two records only. The first was a wrecked bird found at Llanvi-hangel-Ystern-Llewern on 7th September 1967, which was ringed and then released on Steep Holm on 23rd September, only to be found dead on the South Wales coast two weeks later. The second record is of a solitary bird seen at the mouth of the Wye, flying back and forth across the river between Gwent and Gloucestershire on 19th August 1969.

27 **GANNET** *Sula bassana*

Formerly a very uncommon visitor, but almost annual in recent years. Seventeen individuals have been recorded in the county, mostly from April to September, but occasionally in winter. About half of these were immature birds, and all were singles with the exception of one very old record (September 1893) of four on Denny Island.

Five of the birds were recorded as being injured or exhausted, including one on a mountain near Pontypool on 4th November 1960, and in addition, many of the coastal and offshore sightings followed periods of bad weather. Gannets have been seen flying in both directions in the channel, e.g. one downchannel off Peterstone Wentlooge on 28th May 1973 and one upchannel off Collister Pill on 7th September 1974. There was a very unusual record in 1972 of an adult flying down the Wye about half a mile upstream from Monmouth.

28 **CORMORANT** *Phalacrocorax carbo*

Resident and winter visitor. There is no confirmed record of breeding, but a nest, believed to be that of a Cormorant, was found on Denny Island on 17th June 1963 (Boyd, 1963). Birds are found throughout the year on the coast and at inland waters, peak numbers of approximately 50 being recorded in most winters. The largest count, however, was of 70 in flight in the Usk valley near Llantrisant on 19th February 1974. Much smaller numbers of non-breeders remain during the summer. Although the species penetrates well inland along the river basins, the number of individuals seen at any one inland site is usually small, and in the 1960s only once went into double figures (15 at Kemeys Inferior in January 1969). In recent years, however, the inland numbers have increased markedly, for example, the maxima at Llandegfedd Reservoir have been four in February and December 1971, nine in April 1972, 24 in December 1973 and 20 in December 1974. It is also a regular visitor to most other inland lakes and reservoirs.

Most of the large counts come from roosts and there are a number of long established sites in the county, e.g. the " Cormorant tree " at Llangybi (18 birds in January 1970), Piercefield Cliffs on the river Wye, Denny Island (17 on the east face in April 1968), Newport Docks (24 in March 1967) and Newbridge-on-Usk (18 in February 1974). When they are feeding, birds from these roosts spread out along the rivers and the coast and thus small numbers are likely to be seen at such places at any time, reaching as far inland as the Monnow above Monmouth.

29 **SHAG** *Phalacrocorax aristotelis*

Three records only. One was shot at Uskmouth in February 1907 and another, which had been ringed on Anglesey on 2nd June 1938, was recovered in Newport on 11th October 1938. Two immature birds found at Llantarnam on 13th March 1962 were part of the widespread wreck of birds crossing from the east coast which occurred that year.

30 **HERON** *Ardea cinerea*

Resident breeding species. There are three well established heronries at present, at Pant-y-Goitre, Whitson and Piercefield Woods which hold about 70 pairs between them. This may not be the maximum, as occasional small heronries containing one or two nests are also noted from time to time. This is particularly true in the years which follow the felling of a major heronry wood as happened very recently at Part-y-seal which held 20 nests in 1975. Sometimes these small colonies grow to become major ones. Out of season, it is observed widely, usually in groups of less than six but as many as 16 have been seen together at Llandegfedd Reservoir and Llanvihangel Gobion.

38 BITTERN *Botaurus stellaris*

Rare winter visitor. All early records were of shot birds (nine altogether between 1889 and 1926). In recent years, single birds were seen at Goldcliff on 24th October 1967 and at Malpas on 3rd May 1968, while the remains of another were discovered near Uskmouth in November 1969.

42 SPOONBILL *Platalea leucorodia*

The only record is of up to three birds seen on various dates in June 1973 at Peterstone Wentlooge; this occurrence coincides with reports of the species elsewhere in Britain.

43 GLOSSY IBIS *Plegadis falcinellus*

The only record is of an adult male shot between Newport and Caerleon on 11th October 1902 and subsequently on display in Newport Museum.

45 MALLARD *Anas platyrhynchos*

Common resident, breeding in suitable localities throughout the county. That breeding may occur up to at least 390 m (1300 ft.) above sea-level would seem to be indicated from a record of a duck with six ducklings crossing the Heads of the Valleys road at this elevation on 1st July 1974. Up to 20 pairs have bred at Llandegfedd Reservoir.

Varying numbers are to be seen on the coast throughout the year, the lowest figures tending to be in November and December. A total of between 200 and 300 non-breeding birds remains throughout spring and summer, increasing in August owing, presumably, to the arrival of young birds and adults which have finished breeding. The largest coastal flocks, in fact, tend to occur in August (290 in 1973; 400 in 1974, at Peterstone Wentlooge), although on 9th December 1973, 690 were counted between Uskmouth and Peterstone.

The largest winter gatherings now occur on Llandegfedd Reservoir, with totals up to 1200 and 1300 since 1969, when the numbers suddenly doubled over those of previous winters. The highest numbers occur from November to February, with the peak in December and January.

46 TEAL *Anas crecca*

Common visitor, mainly in winter and on passage, especially on the coast and in the Usk valley. The species has bred in the county, the first record being of two pairs nesting at Llandowlais in 1943, but its breeding status is uncertain and further information is badly needed.

In general, it occurs from August until April. The largest numbers are found in December and January at Llandegfedd Reservoir, where counts usually range from 100 to 200, and on the coast where exceptionally, 300–400 occur in these two months. Ynysyfro Reservoir may hold up to around 20 in the winter months, although there were 180 there in November 1969. Parties of 20–30, and occasionally up to 100, occur from time to time in the Usk valley and on flooded areas inland.

A bird ringed in Swedish Lapland on 17th May 1956 was recovered at Newport on 1st January 1958, while another ringed in the Camargue on 9th February 1959 was recovered at Newport on 18th September 1959.

47 GARGANEY *Anas querquedula*

Has bred twice in the county; otherwise, an uncommon passage migrant. Breeding is only known to have occurred in the south of the county, the first record (and the first for Wales for more than 20 years) having been in 1965, and the second in 1969, when a duck was seen with eight or nine young.

Parties of up to five occur on passage from March to May and again from July to September, mostly in the coastal areas. It has also occurred at Llandegfedd Reservoir in October 1967 (three birds) and March 1968 (five birds).

49 GADWALL *Anas strepera*

Uncommon but regular passage migrant and winter visitor. Before 1967 the only documented record is of a bird shot at Rumney (Monmouthshire) on 12th October 1954. Since 1967 it has been recorded in every winter season, with an annual average of three records. Of these, nine have been in the period August–October, eight in the period February–April, five in December and one in June.

It occurs chiefly at Llandegfedd Reservoir and along the coast from Peterstone Wentlooge to Undy, but also occasionally at Magor, usually in ones or twos, sometimes up to four, and exceptionally seven at Peterstone on 22nd June 1974 and eight at Magor on 26th October 1969. Elsewhere, pairs have occurred once each at St. Pierre Lake and Pant-yr- eos Reservoir.

It has been suggested (Heathcote, Griffin and Salmon, 1967; Lewis, 1968) that the recent increase of this species in S. Wales has resulted from the spread of feral populations in other parts of the country.

50 WIGEON *Anas penelope*

Winter visitor in considerable numbers. It was reported as having bred in the south of the county from 1965 to 1968; these are the only county breeding records and possibly also the first for S. Wales.

The winter flocks start to build up in October, with a considerable increase in numbers in November; the peaks are reached usually in December and January with numbers staying fairly high in February and often well into March. Up to 1966, the largest gatherings were in the

Caldicot Moor and Undy area, but since this time they have steadily declined there, often not exceeding 100 now, although occasionally they rise to 200 or 300. The numbers at Llandegfedd Reservoir, on the other hand, have increased steadily since 1967: the usual November–February range has been from 250 to 700, with exceptionally, 1,000 in January 1974 and 1,300 on 22nd December 1975.

Flocks of up to 60 also occur on floodwater in the Usk valley, while small numbers, up to eight, have occurred at Garnlydan, Ynysyfro and Cwm Tyleri Reservoirs.

52 **PINTAIL** *Anas acuta*

Regular and fairly common winter visitor, mainly to the coast, but also to one or two inland waters. Numbers are usually small, but are subject to considerable fluctuation from one year to another. Thus, in late February and throughout March 1962, there were about 45 present on Caldicot Levels, with comparable numbers in January – March 1965 and 1966, but this figure was not approached again until February 1971, when there were 40 at Undy. At Peterstone Wentlooge there were 100 in February and 60 in October 1972 and 65 in December 1975. On spring passage it has occurred as late as May and on autumn passage, usually from August onwards. Exceptionally, one was seen at Peterstone in July 1974. On inland waters, it has been reported at Llandegfedd Reservoir in almost every year since 1967, the highest numbers being 12 in January 1969 and 14 in January 1975. The only other reservoir on which it has been reported is Ynysyfro where one occurred on 7th December 1969.

53 **SHOVELER** *Anas clypeata*

Frequent winter visitor in quite large numbers; rarely breeds. The only definite breeding record is for 1966, when a duck with six young was seen at Undy Pool on 6th July but pairs were also seen at Magor in April in 1969 and 1970.

Humphreys (1963) commented that, while formerly uncommon, it was then being seen regularly in numbers up to 200 (presumably on the coast). Although no gatherings of this size have been reported since 1963, the largest numbers occur on the coast at Peterstone Wentlooge, usually between October and March. In 1973 and 1974 the numbers there in November and February ranged from about 60 to 90 and in December and January from 110 to about 160. In 1975, however, they were down to 50 or less.

Inland records come from Llandegfedd Reservoir, where it was first recorded in 1968, again in 1969, and annually since 1972, and also from Ynysyfro and Wentwood Reservoirs. Apart from 28 females at Ynysyfro on 12th November 1970, parties have not exceeded six.

54 RED-CRESTED POCHARD *Netta rufina*

The only record is of a single male at Ynysyfro Reservoir on 22nd December 1972. The likelihood of this bird having escaped from a collection is of course considerable.

55 SCAUP *Aythya marila*

Winter visitor and passage migrant in small numbers; occasionally recorded in summer. Detailed records date only from 1966. However, Heathcote, Griffin and Salmon (1967) stated that at the end of the last century this species occurred in flocks in the Severn and was regarded as the most numerous of its genus, while Ingram and Salmon (1939) described it as a regular visitor to the Monmouthshire coast, sometimes in considerable numbers.

Since 1966, about 190 individuals have been recorded with over 150 in the period October–February and of these, about half in December. The bulk of records are from the coast, particularly Peterstone Wentlooge, where in two years of intensive observation during 1973 and 1974, the species was recorded in every month of the year and rather more than half the county total since 1966 was seen. Elsewhere, there are records in most years from one or more of the inland waters, particularly Wentwood and Llandegfedd Reservoirs. Whether they are coastal or inland, records generally concern fewer than five birds, occasionally a few more, though at Peterstone flocks of 20 were seen in December in both 1966 and 1973, 15 in January 1973 and exceptionally 12 at Wentwood Reservoir in November 1971.

On passage, up to four birds have been seen at Peterstone in April and early May, and again from 26th August to 5th September in each of the years 1973–75. Summer records comprise a single male at Peterstone in July 1968 and another seen there on many dates from 20th May to 29th July 1973. Additionally, a party of two adults and three juveniles at Llandegfedd on 11th May 1970 showed the characters of this species.

56 TUFTED DUCK *Aythya fuligula*

Autumn to spring visitor in moderate to large numbers; a few remain during summer. Although it has always been regular in its occurrence, it was formerly not very numerous and the increase to its present strength occurred between 1965 and 1968, when successive annual maxima at Llandegfedd Reservoir were 30, 50, 80 and 180. A similar increase at Ynysyfro Reservoir dates from about the same period and since 1969 these two reservoirs have, between them, held about 90% of the county total with maxima of 100–150 at Llandegfedd and 45–200 at Ynysyfro. Substantial numbers often arrive in September, e.g. 58 at Llandegfedd in 1974, and the maximum may occur in any month from October to March though most often in December or January, and flocks of more than 50 are not usually recorded after March. Although records from May to August used to be very irregular, in the last four years a few birds have remained at Llandegfedd throughout this period.

Wentwood Reservoir is the only other water frequented regularly and during the winter period generally holds 10 to 20 birds, occasionally up to 30. Elsewhere, flocks of up to about ten occur irregularly on most inland waters, including parts of the Usk, and similarly on the coast. Exceptionally, about 50 were sighted offshore at Peterstone Wentlooge in February 1952.

It has not been known to breed in Gwent, although in the neighbouring counties of Glamorgan, Gloucestershire and Somerset it has been an established breeder for many years.

57 POCHARD *Aythya ferina*

Mainly a winter visitor in fairly large numbers. It was previously described as the commonest diving duck (Humphreys, 1963) but in some recent winters the Tufted Duck has been equally, if not more, numerous.

Its main haunt is Llandegfedd Reservoir where numbers generally reach double figures in September, increase to a maximum in December or January and decrease to single figures again by April. The size of the winter maximum increased during the mid-1960s to c400 in 1968 but has since decreased and in each of years 1973–75 has been c150. It is also recorded regularly at Wentwood Reservoir, where, since 1961, the winter maximum has generally been around 50, though as high as c100 in 1969 and c125 in 1961. Similar numbers occur regularly at Ynysyfro Reservoir, but with an exceptionally high maximum of c220 in the winter of 1972–73. At other inland waters it is scarce and irregular, though as many as 27 were observed at Garnlydan Reservoir in 1969 and 23 on the River Usk at Llanbadoc in 1974. Although Caldicot Moor was flooded annually prior to recent drainage, the presence there of up to c200 and c80 in the winters of 1965–66 and 1966–67 was very unusual.

58 FERRUGINOUS DUCK *Aythya nyroca*

The only definite record is of an immature seen at Pant-yr-eos Reservoir on 28th October and 3rd November 1973, although a bird at Llandegfedd Reservoir on 30th October 1965 was, very probably, also this species.

60 GOLDENEYE *Bucephala clangula*

Mainly a winter visitor in small numbers. It is regularly recorded at Llandegfedd Reservoir, usually from November to March, and in numbers of up to c20. It also occurs occasionally on the Usk from Llanwenarth down to Kemeys Inferior, and irregularly at other inland waters and on the coast, usually in ones or twos, but occasionally up to eight together.

Although a few birds sometimes linger until April, most records in this month, as also in October, September and (once) August, tend to be isolated occurrences, more indicative of passage than early arrival or late departure.

61 LONG-TAILED DUCK *Clangula hyemalis*

Winter visitor and passage migrant, rare, but fairly regular in recent years. The total of ten records, all since 1965, includes some lengthy stays ranging from one to over four months. Three of these have been at Llandegfedd Reservoir, where, in the winter of 1966–67, a female was present from 18th December to 1st March; in 1969–70, two birds from 30th November to 28th December, with one remaining until 9th April, and in 1970, a male throughout December. At Pant-yr-eos Reservoir a male stayed from 27th March to 24th April 1973.

Of the more transitory occurrences, five have involved one or two birds present for periods of up to two days (twice each in November and February, once in April) at Llandegfedd, Wentwood Reservoir, or on the coast at Undy, and the sixth, a bird which stayed on the temporarily-flooded Gout at Peterstone Wentlooge from 17th to 23rd October 1975.

62 VELVET SCOTER *Melanitta fusca*

Three records only: the first concerns an immature female shot near Peterstone Wentlooge on 29th December 1938, and the others are of single birds, both in 1970, flying down-channel at Goldcliff on 26th October and at Peterstone on 7th December.

64 COMMON SCOTER *Melanitta nigra*

Regular offshore in small to moderate numbers, mainly from July to April; occasional inland. It was described by Ingram and Salmon (1939) as a regular winter visitor to the coast, sometimes in large flocks. Intensive coastal observation since 1972, particularly at Peterstone Wentlooge, has indicated that although numbers have almost certainly decreased, records are no longer limited to winter. Arrival begins in July when parties of up to six have frequently been seen and though records have been a little scarcer in August and September, they have increased again from October onwards with maximum flock sizes of 20 at Undy in October 1973, *c*26 at Peterstone during November and December 1974, and 18 at Peterstone in December 1975. Since 1964, records in the early part of the year have been very scarce, but in 1975 flocks of up to 16 were regularly reported from Peterstone in the period January–April. There are only two May records and about six in June, each involving one or two birds, except for six at Peterstone on 2nd June 1973.

Inland, one to four birds have been seen during the period July–December on three occasions each at Llandegfedd and Ynysyfro Reservoirs, and exceptionally 11 at the former water on 12th April 1974.

67 **EIDER** *Somateria mollissima*

Two records only. A male was shot at Pant-yr-eos Reservoir in the winter of 1894–95 and a female was seen offshore at Peterstone Wentlooge on 27th September 1974. Moderate numbers of this species are present throughout the year as near as Whiteford Point, W. Glamorgan, but are only very rarely recorded outside its immediate vicinity.

69 **RED-BREASTED MERGANSER** *Mergus serrator*

Regular visitor in small numbers, usually in winter or spring. Two were seen at the mouth of the Usk in 1920 and no more until 1968. Since then, there have been several records in almost every winter–spring period (October–May), though only two in the three periods 1970–71 to 1972–73. Most have been at Llandegfedd Reservoir, though several also from the coast, Uskmouth ash ponds and the Usk at Kemeys Inferior, and one at Ynysyfro Reservoir. Records seldom refer to more than five birds, though eleven " redheads " were seen on the Usk in March 1970.

70 **GOOSANDER** *Mergus merganser*

Regular winter visitor in small to moderate numbers; has recently bred. Before 1963 it was a very irregular visitor (Humphreys, 1963) there being only eight records (seven of single birds and one pair) during the period 1896–1945. However, a flock of eight was observed on the Usk at Llancayo in January 1963, and since 1966 it has been recorded in increasing numbers and with increasing frequency, chiefly from Llandegfedd Reservoir, but also from the Usk between Llanwenarth and Newbridge-on-Usk. Most records have been in the period December–March, with a few in November, April–June and September. In most years since 1969 maximum numbers at Llandegfedd have been between 10 and 15, but in 1974 there were flocks of 17 in January, 51 in February and 23 in March, while on the Usk flocks have usually comprised fewer than five birds, but occasionally up to ten. Parties of up to three have also been recorded six times at Ynysyfro Reservoir, and once each at Garnlydan, Cwm Tyleri, Pant-yr-eos and Wentwood Reservoirs. Most exceptionally, 35 were observed on the mud-flats at Peterstone Wentlooge on 18th September 1968.

A family party containing 11 chicks, 10 of which later flew, was observed within the county on several occasions during June and July 1975. This is only the second breeding record for Wales and the most southerly in the British Isles.

71 **SMEW** *Mergus albellus*

Rare and irregular winter visitor. Apart from a female which was shot near Rumney (Monmouthshire) in December 1938, all records are very recent and involve a total of probably no more than four birds. At

Llandegfedd Reservoir in 1970, a female was present on 5th January, a male on 8th February, and a male and a female on 15th February. At the same water in 1974, there were records of a female on 8th, 18th and 30th December which probably all referred to the same bird. Another female was seen offshore at Peterstone Wentlooge on 3rd January 1973.

73 SHELDUCK *Tadorna tadorna*

Resident and breeds in fairly small numbers; winter visitor in large numbers. Although nests are seldom found, successful breeding, all along the coastal strip, becomes apparent when parents lead their broods out on to the mud-flats in late June and July. This is soon followed by the merging of broods into large " nursery groups " under the control of single parental pairs. As a result, the original number of broods can only be guessed at, but about ten annually seems a reasonable estimate. The most favoured feeding areas for these groups are Peterstone Wentlooge where as many as 37 juveniles were present in 1973, and the Undy–Magor region where the total is often around 30.

Outside the breeding season, much greater numbers are seen at most coastal localities but the largest concentrations are again usually seen at Undy and at Peterstone and St. Brides Wentlooge. In all regions, numbers are low in the autumn, consisting mainly of locally-reared juveniles and seldom exceeding $c50$ from August to October. From November onwards flocks swell rapidly and from December to March or even April, they commonly contain from $c100$ to $c300$ birds. After a peak, usually in February or March, numbers in the Peterstone–St. Brides region decline rapidly to a handful of summering birds, but at Undy, the high winter numbers are in many years maintained through the spring and actually increase further to give the years highest totals in June and July. In 1974 the total population at Undy exceeded 400 in both these months, before declining to the low autumn figures characteristic of the coast as a whole.

Inland, up to four birds (once seven) are recorded almost annually at Llandegfedd Reservoir, usually in April, but occasionally also in March, January and October. Similar numbers are occasionally recorded from other inland waters, virtually always in April or May.

74 RUDDY SHELDUCK *Tadorna ferruginea*

The only record is of one offshore at Undy on 23rd May 1965. This species is now widely kept in captivity and there is always a strong possibility that records involve escaped birds.

75 GREYLAG GOOSE *Anser anser*

Three records only, of single birds at Llandegfedd Reservoir on 5th September 1967, at Llanfoist on 22nd April 1974 and at Collister Pill on 29th May 1975; the dates suggest that any of these could have been escapes.

76 WHITE-FRONTED GOOSE *Anser albifrons*

Regular winter visitor, usually in moderate numbers. The county's records undoubtedly represent local movements associated with the flocks of several thousand which have their main wintering quarters around Slimbridge. Numbers recorded vary considerably from year to year, but flocks of up to about 80 birds are frequently seen. One exceptionally large flock, of about 1000 birds, was seen over Abergavenny on 7th March 1969; there are also three records of flocks of up to 200 birds.

Most of the records are of sightings in the low-lying coastal areas, particularly around Magor and Caldicot, and in the Usk valley. Sightings are most frequent in mid-winter (two-thirds of all records are in December or January), fairly frequent up to the end of April and occasional in October and November.

There is one definite record of a bird of the Greenland race *A.a. flavirostris*, at Llandegfedd Reservoir in March 1974.

78 PINK-FOOTED GOOSE *Anser fabalis*

Rare winter visitor at present. Two earlier reports, of " many " at Llanwern in October–December 1899 and " three large flocks " at Peterstone Wentlooge in December 1935, suggest that it could have been a more frequent visitor in the past.

The only recent records are of one on Rumney levels (Monmouthshire) on 3rd February 1963, one at Undy on 25th December 1970 and a flock of 12 at Peterstone on 9th November 1975.

80 BRENT GOOSE *Branta bernicla*

Rare winter visitor, recorded three times in pre-war years and twice recently. Of these records, two refer to the dark-breasted race *B.b.bernicla:* the first, of one " seen and clearly identified " (but no further data available) on 16th January 1928 (Ingram and Salmon, 1939) and the second, two sightings on 23rd January 1972 of (presumably) the same bird by separate observers at Undy and Magor.

The single record of a bird of the light-breasted race *B.b.hrota* is of one shot at Goldcliff on 10th January 1928 (Ingram and Salmon, 1939). For the remaining two records, of a flock of 70 off Goldcliff in February 1929 and 8 off Undy on 14th October 1972, the race could not be ascertained.

81 BARNACLE GOOSE *Branta leucopsis*

The only record is of a single bird on the river Usk at Llanbadoc on 10th October 1970; this could have been an escape.

82 **CANADA GOOSE** *Branta canadensis*

Introduced to the county by the Newport Wildfowling and Gun Club in 1960, with reinforcements in 1962. There is only one record before this, of five at the mouth of the Rhymney (Monmouthshire) in 1866.

Since 1962 records have shown a steady decline in numbers, from flocks of up to 40 in 1963 to one record of a single bird in each year from 1970 to 1972. This decline shows a marked contrast to the success of the vast majority of introductions elsewhere in Britain, and has been attributed to heavy shooting along the coast. There was a suggestion of a recovery of numbers in 1973; the six records include flocks of 20 at Chepstow in October and 12 over Abergavenny in December. The recovery did not appear to be maintained during 1974 and 1975; the only records were of a party of four seen on several occasions on the western outskirts of Newport, two at Llandegfedd Reservoir in January 1974 and one at Collister Pill in September 1975.

There are only a few breeding records: at Newbridge-on-Usk from 1964 to 1969 and at Undy Pool in 1968.

84 **MUTE SWAN** *Cygnus olor*

Breeding resident in moderate numbers. It was formerly described as a common resident, breeding in suitable localities throughout the county (Humphreys, 1963), but it appears that its numbers have declined during the early 1960s and stabilised since then.

The Mute Swan census of 1955–56 reported totals of 17 and 13 nests respectively in these two years. Compared to this, numbers of pairs breeding since 1968 have varied between 5 and 11, from 20 sites spread over the county, though it is possible that the difference may merely reflect less complete observation of the breeding areas than in the census years.

Mute Swans are also regularly seen throughout the county through the whole year, but usually only in ones and twos, with rarely more than 12 together in recent years. Both the 1956 census figure of about 150 non-breeding birds, and the reported gathering of " large numbers " on the Usk in late summer and early autumn in the 1950s, would represent exceptional numbers compared with its present status.

85 **WHOOPER SWAN** *Cygnus cygnus*

Fairly regular winter visitor in recent years, though usually only in small numbers. Although first recorded as recently as February 1960 at Caldicot and Llanmartin, there have subsequently been 23 records of this species in 11 of the 16 winters 1959–60 to 1974–75. The dates of these records are fairly evenly spread over the winter months, the earliest and latest being 29th October and 8th March respectively.

They are usually seen in small numbers, rarely more than ten together; the largest flocks reported were of 24 at Caerwent in 1969 and 25 at Llandegfedd Reservoir in 1972. Nearly all the sightings have been in the low-lying coastal and Usk valley areas; one notable exception being of two at Pen-y-fan Pond in January and February 1971.

86 BEWICK'S SWAN *Cygnus bewickii*

Regular winter visitor in recent years, in moderate and probably increasing numbers.

There are only two records before 1962, of a bird found dead near Newport in November 1909, and of two seen (locality unnamed) in February 1960. Since then, significant numbers have been recorded in the winters of 1961–62, 1965–66 and every winter since 1967–68; the totals having built up from about 20 in the early years to about 70 in 1973–74 and about 60 in 1974–75.

Until 1971 the bulk of the records were from the Caldicot area, with only sporadic sightings elsewhere, but since then the species has been regularly seen in increasing numbers both at Llandegfedd Reservoir and on flooded water-meadows in the area between Newbridge-on-Usk and Llandenny. In nearly all years the greatest numbers have been seen between mid-December and March, usually reaching a maximum in February with flocks of up to about 30, and with occasional sightings from October and into April.

It seems very probable that these increases reflect overspill from the larger flocks which visit the area around Slimbridge (Glos.) during the winter.

91 BUZZARD *Buteo buteo*

At present a widespread and successful breeding species in moderate numbers. Considered doubtfully resident in the county in 1939 (Ingram and Salmon, 1939), its numbers increased during and after the war and it is at present widely reported every year with a breeding population of about 25 pairs. Most of these are in the central and northern areas of the county, but there have been occasional reports from the industrial valleys of the north-west. By contrast it is absent, or at best rare, as a breeding species in the low-lying coastal areas and in the south-eastern part of the county; in the latter area a sharp decrease in numbers around 1960 has been attributed to illegal shooting.

Reports of sightings outside the breeding season are widespread and numerous, often of parties of up to eight.

92 ROUGH-LEGGED BUZZARD *Buteo lagopus*

The only record is of one seen at Crick on 21st January 1973.

93 SPARROWHAWK *Accipiter nisus*

Resident, and at present breeds in moderate numbers. It was considered to be a common species in the pre-war years, but records for the county during the 1950s reflect the trend throughout Britain of a drastic decline in numbers, to rarity status in the early 1960s (Humphreys, 1963). However, an encouraging increase in reports began in 1965, reaching a stable level of about 12 breeding pairs from 1969 to 1973. It remains to be seen whether the low number of breeding records in 1974 and 1975 (only two in each year) represents a real decline in numbers or merely incomplete recording.

The strongholds of the species appear to be the areas around Abergavenny and the central districts. It is, however, regularly reported from many other areas, notably around Caldicot where it has bred regularly for several years, and in the vicinity of Newport. Recently there have also been reports from the industrial valleys of the north-west.

Reports outside the breeding season are frequent, often of single birds, though occasionally up to three have been seen together.

94 GOSHAWK *Accipiter gentilis*

Rare visitor. The possibility of escaped birds can never be entirely ruled out, but there are a number of records, all in recent years, for which there is no evidence of their being escapes. In three instances a bird remained in the Wentwood area for several weeks, in March and May 1971, in August 1974 and in the summer of 1975; there were also several sightings between Wentwood and Monkswood in March and April 1975.

The remaining records are isolated sightings of single birds: at Llanellen on 11th June 1966; at Peterstone Wentlooge 17–22nd August 1973 and in mid-July 1974; at Parc Seymour on 20th September 1973; and at Abergavenny on 27th October 1974.

There are also four records in recent years, of which two certainly, and the other two very probably, involve escaped birds.

95 RED KITE *Milvus milvus*

At present only an occasional visitor. It was formerly recorded as having bred at Nantyderry in about 1870; also two specimens in Newport Museum, from the Tredegar collection, are said to have been shot locally.

Kites have been recorded annually since 1968; the eleven records in eight years have all been of single birds, during the periods March–April and June–September, with one in November, in localities fairly widespread through the county.

98 HONEY BUZZARD *Pernis apivorus*

The only recent record is of one seen over St. Mary's Vale, Abergavenny, on 10th June 1975. [A record in the 1900 edition of *The Birds of Glamorgan* (quoted in Ingram and Salmon, 1939) refers to " one obtained some years ago in Machen Wood," without any further data.]

99 MARSH HARRIER *Circus aeruginosus*

Rare passage migrant. Each of the four records involves a single female bird, the sightings being at Peterstone Wentlooge on 31st August 1958 and again on 13th September 1969, at Goldcliff on 28th April 1968 and at St. Brides Wentlooge on 19th May 1973. These dates clearly suggest birds on passage; it is interesting to note that the record for April 1968 coincided with a period of unusually numerous sightings at Cley, on the north Norfolk coast, and a subsequent wide scattering of records elsewhere in Britain, including two from Ireland (*British Birds*, vol. 61, nos. 6 and 7, pp 279 and 328: 1968).

100 HEN HARRIER *Circus cyaneus*

Uncommon winter visitor and passage migrant. Although recorded only rarely up to about ten years ago, there are records for eight of the ten winters since 1966–67, the average being two records per year. Apart from two during April–May, the sightings have been fairly evenly spread over the months September–February. In nearly all cases a single bird was seen, at various localities in the low-lying coastal areas and the Usk valley. The one exception is a remarkable record of a group of ten birds seen flying south along the west side of the Skirrid Fawr on 16th September 1974.

102 MONTAGU'S HARRIER *Circus pygargus*

Rare and irregular visitor. Two records in recent years suggest birds remaining in one area of the county for several weeks: a pair at Wentwood in May and June 1968 and a single bird at Pontllanfraith in May and early June 1973. Another record, of one on the Sugar Loaf on 9th June 1973 could well have been the latter bird wandering further afield.

The remaining records are more indicative of birds on passage: these are, of single birds at Peterstone Wentlooge on 21st September 1935, 12th October 1964 and 3rd April 1967; a pair flying along the ridge at Bertholey on 25th August 1968 and single birds at Pant-yr-eos Reservoir on 27th July 1972 and at Tintern on 26th April 1974.

103 OSPREY *Pandion haliaetus*

Recorded annually as a passage migrant from 1965 to 1974, although usually with only one or two sightings each year.

On spring passage single birds have been seen near Monmouth in April of each year from 1968 to 1972, with a pair seen in this area early in May 1973. Two other single birds have been seen on spring passage, at Wentwood Reservoir in April 1969 and near Usk on the extraordinarily early date of 23rd February 1973.

Autumn passage records have nearly all been of single birds seen either over the upper reaches of the river Usk or at Llandegfedd Reservoir, the one exception being at Penhow on 18th August 1974. These have been seen in eight of the eleven years 1965 to 1975, all within the period 18th August to 13th September, and in nearly all cases closely preceded by reports from southern Powys, usually from Llangorse Lake or Talybont Reservoir, of what has probably been the same bird in each case.

104 **HOBBY** *Falco subbuteo*

Formerly a rare breeder, now only an occasional summer visitor and passage migrant. There are three records of breeding from pre-war years, at Wentwood in 1910 and near Usk and near Chepstow in the 1930s; in both the latter cases the birds were shot. A pair also probably bred in 1966, being seen several times in the same area. Otherwise up to 1975 there are 17 records of the species, 15 of them since 1966, of a single bird on each occasion, and mainly from scattered localities in the Usk valley. The sightings are fairly evenly distributed over the period early April – late October, apart from one remarkably late record of a bird at Llanover on 4th December 1975; however, it is possible that this could have been an escaped bird.

105 **PEREGRINE** *Falco peregrinus*

Fairly regular visitor, both in winter and on passage, but always in small numbers. Of the 27 records for the years 1966 to 1973 and 1975, about two-thirds are in the migration months March–May and September –October, the remaining one-third being in the winter. The eleven records for 1974 are, exceptionally, nearly all in the winter, and if combined with those of 1966–73 and 1975 would raise the proportion of winter records to about half the total. Some birds evidently stay for prolonged periods: one at Llangattock cliffs (Powys) in the spring of 1969 was frequently seen over the Usk valley near Abergavenny, while another was regularly seen in the Wentwood area in the winter of 1970–71.

Earlier records are of occasional winter sightings along the coast, in contrast to those of recent years which show a much greater geographical spread over the county.

There is only one definite record of attempted breeding, on Denny Island in 1927 (Humphreys, 1963).

107 **MERLIN** *Falco columbarius*

At present recorded in small numbers at all seasons but breeds only irregularly. There is only one definite record of breeding since 1965, but many years ago it was considered to be regularly resident in the hills, although definite breeding was recorded only once, near Blaenavon about 1900 (Humphreys, 1963).

However, it is regularly seen throughout the county in small numbers, with an average of nine records annually in recent years. These are almost equally divided between the hills of the north-west, the low-lying coastal areas and the rest of the county. Only along the coast is there a marked seasonal bias, where nearly all the records are in the winter period November–February, whereas elsewhere the records are fairly evenly spread through the year.

110 KESTREL *Falco tinnunculus*

Common and widely distributed breeding species in a great variety of habitats. The breeding records received in recent years (average 11 annually, maximum 17) almost certainly underestimate the breeding population.

Outside the breeding season Kestrels are frequently seen throughout the county, usually singly, but occasionally in parties of up to ten, especially in late summer and autumn. Two exceptionally large flocks recorded are of 20 over Twmbarlwm in July 1971 and at least 15 near the Rhymney estuary (Monmouthshire) on 30th August 1972.

111 RED GROUSE *Lagopus lagopus*

At present widespread and regularly seen on the high ground in the north-west, though usually only in small numbers. In the late nineteenth century the grouse on the Blaenavon moors were preserved as game, the population then being probably well over 1000 birds. Since the end of preservation the numbers have declined steeply until in 1960 there were at most 10 pairs there. Recent records suggest that Coity Mountain remains one of the main strongholds of the species (35 birds were recorded there in 1970) with other regular sightings, usually only in twos and threes, and only occasionally over ten, reported from most of the other highland areas.

There have also been sporadic records in other parts of the county: one near Newport Docks in May 1968, six at Llandenny in November 1970 and one or two near Peterstone Wentlooge from May to July 1974 and also once in May 1975.

113 BLACK GROUSE *Lyrurus tetrix*

Rare and irregular visitor at present. The only recent records are all of single Blackcocks: on the Blorenge during the winter of 1971–72 and, presumably, the same bird again in September 1972; at Trefil in April 1974 and near Llanthony in May 1974. Black Grouse were formerly described as common in the hills of the north-west in the mid-nineteenth century, mainly in the Llanthony and Sugar Loaf areas, (where they were still seen occasionally up to 1952) and occasionally as far south as Twmbarlwm.

115 RED-LEGGED PARTRIDGE *Alectoris rufa*

Introduced to the county and formerly rare; now recorded more frequently but still irregularly. There is one definite breeding record, at Ponthir in 1973, and two other instances of possible breeding, near

Bassaleg and near Magor in 1971, birds being seen several times in the same area during the breeding season. The 14 remaining records up to the end of 1975 have been isolated sightings, usually of only one or two birds, mainly in the low-lying areas in the coastal region and the Usk valley.

116 PHEASANT 116 PARTRIDGE *Perdix perdix*

Resident breeding species seen regularly through most of the county. In view of the large overall number of sightings definite breeding records (about five annually) are surprisingly few and are almost certainly a considerable underestimate of the actual breeding population. Coveys of up to 20 are regularly seen, especially in the autumn months.

The strongholds of the species appear to be the coastal areas and the Usk valley generally, although they are regularly reported in other areas, notably Monmouth and Cwmavon, while records for the north of the county are comparatively sparse.

117 QUAIL *Coturnix coturnix*

Irregular visitor, mainly in the summer months. There are four breeding records: near Abergavenny and at Caerwent prior to 1900, at Llanvapley in 1965 and at Trostrey in 1967. Otherwise records are irregular (five in three of the eight years 1966–73), usually in the summer months, although there are records of a bird found dead in January 1940 and of one shot in November 1947.

118 PHEASANT *Phasianus colchicus*

Introduced as a game bird many years ago, later described as common only in the areas where it was preserved (Ingram and Salmon, 1939). Recent records reflect some ambiguity; while regularly described as common, even in areas where it was not preserved, the comparatively few breeding records received (up to five pairs annually) hardly confirm this. It would appear that its " unchanged status as a common breeder " has been taken for granted in recent years and may not accurately reflect its true present status. Most records are from the central districts; there are unexpectedly few from the coastal areas.

120 WATER RAIL *Rallus aquaticus*

The habitually secretive behaviour of this species makes its status difficult to ascertain. It seems probable, however, that it breeds in small numbers, with an influx of visitors during the winter.

Water Rails are most often recorded in the area around Abergavenny, from where 40% of all records have been received and where they are also known to breed; two definite breeding records in 1971 at

Llanwenarth Citra and Llanfoist are unlikely to be isolated instances. They are also regularly recorded in the coastal areas, particularly at Peterstone Wentlooge where they bred in 1973, at Magor Reserve and also occasionally elsewhere.

Most records are of small numbers of birds; there are, however, two records of 14 birds, flushed from a marsh at Llanarth in December 1966 and January 1968 respectively. Further evidence for winter immigration comes from two recoveries, of birds ringed in Germany in August 1953 (recovered at Blackwood in January 1955) and at Dungeness in 1963 (recovered at Llanwenarth in March 1964). There is thus a clear indication of a substantial winter influx of birds of continental origin into the county.

121 **SPOTTED CRAKE** *Porzana porzana*

Rare visitor. Ingram and Salmon (1939) suggest that " a few pairs " may have bred early in this century, but there is no substantial evidence to support this opinion. Four definite records from some years ago are of single birds shot near Newport in 1903 and 1917, one seen at Peterstone Wentlooge in August 1940, and one found dead at Llanwern in 1946. The only recent record is of one seen at Peterstone for two weeks in September 1975.

125 **CORNCRAKE** *Crex crex*

At present only a rare and irregular visitor. It was considered to be a well-distributed breeding species, especially in the coastal areas, early in this century, but had declined to a population of only a few pairs by 1938 (Humphreys, 1963). Since then there has been only one definite breeding record, at Llanarth in 1965. There are also three other instances in which birds were heard several times in the same locality during the breeding season: at Llanellen in 1967, at Bulmore in 1968 (where it was known to breed regularly before the war) and at Llangwm in 1972. Other recent records (six in the eight years 1966 to 1973) comprise isolated hearings of single birds, all between mid-August and early October, and suggestive of a small trickle of autumn migration through the county.

126 **MOORHEN** *Gallinula chloropus*

Common and widespread breeding species. It is most frequently found in the reens of the coastal levels and along the Monmouthshire–Brecon canal (clearly the most suitable habitats), but also occurs widely on rivers, ponds and other suitable waters (though not usually on the reservoirs) through most of the county. Only in the industrial valleys of the north-west is it scarce or absent.

Occasional gatherings of moderate numbers in winter have been recorded in recent years: e.g., about 50 at Llanfoist in 1971 and 40 at Abergavenny sewage works in 1967–68.

127 COOT *Fulica atra*

Resident and breeds in small numbers; winter visitor in large numbers. The present breeding population appears to be about 20 pairs altogether; nearly all of these are in either the coastal area between Newport and Undy, the Usk valley between Abergavenny and Usk, or Llandegfedd Reservoir.

In recent years Llandegfedd Reservoir has become an important wintering site for Coot, where they now occur annually in very large numbers. From a maximum of 100 there early in 1964 the winter population has steadily increased to a maximum of about 1,100 in the winter of 1973–74. The first substantial numbers usually arrive in September and stay until the following March. Other waters in the county also have regular wintering flocks but of much smaller numbers; the largest of these are at Undy and Ynysyfro Reservoir, each having maxima of about 50.

131 OYSTERCATCHER *Haematopus ostralegus*

Resident breeder and winter visitor in small numbers. It bred on Denny Island up to 1899. It also attempted to breed at one locality on the Gwent shore from 1971 to 1975, but only in 1971 and 1974 did any eggs hatch successfully.

Due to the absence of suitable coastal feeding sites (cockle and mussel beds), the numbers recorded along the shore are small but nevertheless regular. Peak numbers occur during the spring and autumn passage, with maxima of 30 in March 1971 and at least 60 in September 1968 at Peterstone, 35 at St. Brides in April 1975, 50 at Uskmouth in January 1975, and 80 moving up channel past Collister Pill on 11th May 1975.

Inland records from fields, usually of single birds, are most frequent in autumn. Two or three birds are often seen at Llandegfedd Reservoir during the same period, occasionally also in winter. On the whole the spring passage is more marked than the autumn passage on the shore and *vice-versa* inland. The passage migrants, in common with those of other west coast estuaries, are mainly from breeding areas in northern Britain, Iceland and the Faeroes.

133 LAPWING *Vanellus vanellus*

Resident breeder and winter visitor in considerable numbers. Nests in suitable areas throughout the county, from the moorlands in the north to the coastal levels in the south. Post-breeding flocks of several hundred birds have been recorded from many locations, with no less than 4,500 on the river bank at The Bryn in August 1970. Influxes and movements of birds are noted during most winters, the largest, e.g. 15,000 in fields at Magor and Caldicot in December 1970, being closely associated with cold weather and often preceding it by a day or so. These hard weather movements, which are mainly westwards into Ireland and southwards into France, are additional to the regular annual immigration and passage of birds from Scandinavia and other northerly breeding sites. The wintering population along the shore usually consists of about 3,000 birds.

134 RINGED PLOVER *Charadrius hiaticula*

Predominantly a passage migrant with a small wintering population and an occasional breeding pair. The only breeding records are from a single locality in Newport Docks which was occupied from 1971 to 1973. The site was destroyed by development in 1974.

This species is in the northern part of its wintering range in Britain and is thus not abundant in the county, with peak numbers of about 50 at Peterstone Wentlooge and slightly fewer at Undy. Numbers were higher than usual in 1975 with winter peaks of 92 and 100 respectively at these sites. Numbers build up to a maximum in May when there is a considerable passage of the nominate race which breeds in Britain, Iceland and western Europe, together with representatives of the Greenland and Siberian populations which are somewhat smaller in size but indistinguishable in the field. At the peak of spring passage, about 1,500 birds are present along the Gwent shore, though the return passage in August and September is not so well marked.

There are small but regular numbers of birds recorded inland, with peaks during spring and autumn corresponding to the coastal passage, though in this case autumn records are relatively more frequent. The largest number recorded inland was six at Llandegfedd Reservoir on 12th September 1969.

135 LITTLE RINGED PLOVER *Charadrius dubius*

Uncommon passage migrant. There are only 16 records, 13 of them since 1970 and all of one or two birds only. The majority of these are from Peterstone Wentlooge and the only other sites involved are Abergavenny sewage works and Llandegfedd Reservoir. The sightings are equally divided between the spring and autumn passage, and cover the period 5th April to 14th October. Juveniles have been noted in the autumn passage with one as early as 4th July in 1964.

Some 400 pairs of this species, which winters in southern Africa, spend the summer in Britain. The increase in records over the last few years reflects the expanding breeding range of this bird. Gwent is at present just on the edge of this range, and with suitable habitat in the north of the county, it may not be long before it is added to the breeding list.

139 GREY PLOVER *Pluvialis squatarola*

Fairly common winter visitor. It is most numerous in January or February with the highest count from Undy of 700 birds and from Peterstone Wentlooge of 80, while smaller numbers have occurred at other coastal sites such as Goldcliff and Uskmouth. Additional birds occur on passage in spring and autumn, those in spring often being seen in summer plumage. For example, counts from Peterstone in March 1974, showed numbers rising steadily from 11 on the 3rd to a peak of 80 on the 18th, only to fall quickly down again to about 10 in early April. There is usually a small non-breeding resident population during the summer months consisting of about 30 birds in 1974. Inland records are very uncommon with only one bird seen at Llandegfedd Reservoir, on 10th December 1968, and one at Garnlydan Reservoir on 19th May 1974.

140 **GOLDEN PLOVER** *Pluvialis apricaria*

Winter visitor and passage migrant. This species used to breed on the hills around Abertillery, Tredegar and Abergavenny about 90 years ago. There has been a general contraction in the southern part of the breeding range of the Golden Plover throughout Europe during this period and a corresponding expansion in the north.

Flocks of more than a hundred wintering birds are uncommon. However, in 1970 and 1971 consistently large flocks were observed at Undy, e.g. 1,000 on 25th December 1970, 3,000 in January and 2,000 in March 1971 (c.f. high Lapwing numbers during the same period). Most records refer to less than ten and often to single birds. Coastal records are slightly more common than inland ones and have occurred in all months except June.

The southern race *P.a.apricaria* breeds in Britain, southern Scandinavia and the Baltic. In addition to this sub-species birds of the northern race *P.a.altifrons*, are almost certainly included amongst our winter visitors. The latter have a distinctly blacker belly than the southern form (though birds from Scotland are intermediate) and during spring, when birds in breeding plumage pass through on passage, individuals of this race have been recognised in Gwent.

142 **DOTTEREL** *Eudromias morinellus*

The only record is of a single bird on a small pool at Hafodyrynys on 1st September 1972.

143 **TURNSTONE** *Arenaria interpres*

Winter visitor and passage migrant. Only a small patch at the north-east of the Bedwin Sands and some of the foreshore in the Goldcliff region offer suitable stony and weedy substrate for this species. Consequently the wintering population is small, with a maximum of 200 at Undy in 1968, but usually less than 50, and except for a regular winter flock of 20 or so at Peterstone Wentlooge in 1975 only a handful of records from sites to the west of the Usk. It is fairly regular at Goldcliff, where up to 50 are often observed perched on top of salmon putcher frames.

The spring passage of Turnstone is very marked, and along with the passage of other species, it may vary in timing by as much as two or three weeks each year. Maxima of 700 on 6th May 1971, and 500 in April 1972 have been recorded at Undy. Many of these spring birds are in summer plumage. A few non-breeders remain behind throughout the summer until the much less pronounced autumn passage begins. A similar pattern of occurrence involving much smaller numbers of birds is found at Peterstone Wentlooge. Inland records are uncommon but birds have been recorded in spring or autumn from Llandegfedd, Garnlydan and Ynysyfro Reservoirs.

144 **DOWITCHER** *Limnodromus* sp.

All sightings of this American vagrant were in 1971 at Undy. It is difficult to be sure how many birds were involved except that there were at least two. One was observed with Redshanks on 16th September, two on 18th September and one each on 9th and 30th October. Only about one third of the sightings of this bird in Britain have been identified to species (Short-billed or Long-billed Dowitchers).

145 **SNIPE** *Gallinago gallinago*

Resident breeder and winter visitor. Breeding records have come from Magor Reserve (four pairs in 1965), Ebbw Vale, Garnlydan, Carno Reservoir, the Blorenge, and Pwlldu, and song flights are regularly recorded elsewhere. The maximum numbers are seen at freshwater sites even in winter, though the species is regular on the foreshore, e.g. in the saltmarsh between Collister Pill and Magor Pill with a maximum of 114 on 27th January 1973. Peterstone Wentlooge has regular small numbers with 20 present on 30th December 1971. Records at freshwater sites include, in 1968, at least 200 in flooded fields near Rogiet on 23rd January, at least 100 at Undy Pool on 9th March and 300 flushed from a marsh at Llanarth (no date). 40 were observed in Newport Docks on 4th March 1973 and a maximum at Magor Reserve of 100 in March 1965. Llandegfedd Reservoir supports a regular wintering population which consisted of about ten birds in 1974 with a peak of 50 in December and similar numbers are recorded in most years. Spring and autumn passage was particularly noticeable at this site in 1975 with the year's maxima being 79 in March and nine in September.

147 **JACK SNIPE** *Lymnocryptes minima*

Uncommon winter visitor. All records but one are confined to the period October–March, the exception being an early autumn passage migrant at Peterstone Wentlooge on 26th August 1974. During winter, it is intermittently recorded at Abergavenny sewage works, rubbish tip and golf course, Llandegfedd Reservoir, Garnlydan, Llanarth, Newport Docks and Undy. Most records are of single birds, but three were observed at Llandegfedd on 15th December 1974; and above average numbers (no figure quoted) were reported from Llanarth in 1968 — the year when large numbers of Common Snipe were observed at this locality.

148 **WOODCOCK** *Scolopax rusticola*

Scarce breeding resident. During recent years it has bred successfully on the Sugar Loaf, Skirrid Fach, at Cwmyoy, Wentwood and Reddings Inclosure, whilst roding has been reported from many other areas. It has been even more widely reported during winter in small numbers, with occasional larger congregations such as the ten recorded near Cwmyoy in December 1968. In winter, the resident British population is swollen by the arrival of continental immigrants which may account for a substantial proportion of the winter records in Gwent.

150 **CURLEW** *Numenius arquata*

Resident local breeder, common passage migrant and winter visitor. Breeding has been recorded widely over the north and west of the county. With widespread breeding also occurring in neighbouring counties, it is not surprising that peak numbers are recorded on the Gwent coast during July and August when the young of the year congregate there. At Undy, for example, maxima of 1,000 were recorded on 29th August 1969 and 550 in August 1974. Numbers then decrease during late autumn until the wintering population levels are reached, which in the case of Undy may be from 200 to 400 birds. A similar pattern is observed at other coastal sites, the greatest wintering population at Peterstone Wentlooge being 200 in October 1968.

Spring passage is particularly noticeable since migrating birds often fly at low altitude. For example, a large movement was recorded over Abergavenny during the night of 14th–15th March 1972. At Llandegfedd Reservoir, only single birds have been recorded in winter, but up to 16 have occurred during the spring passage period and there is a similar pattern at other inland sites. A few non-breeders remain on the coast throughout the summer.

151 **WHIMBREL** *Numenius phaeopus*

Regular spring and autumn passage migrant. As with the Ringed Plover and Turnstone it is the spring passage which predominates. The maximum number recorded for the whole of the Gwent shore in any one autumn is only just over 30, whereas 1,000 were observed at Undy alone on 1st May 1976. Other high numbers include 250 in May 1975 at Undy, 152 at Peterstone Wentlooge in May 1975 and 74 on the banks of the Usk at Caerleon on 2nd May 1971. The main passage period extends from April to September with only occasional records in June. The earliest record is on 20th March and the latest on 11th October. Inland records include several of nocturnal passage, during both spring and autumn, over

91

Abergavenny and Cwmbran. Maxima at the inland waters are six at Llandegfedd Reservoir on 20th April 1968 and again at Garnlydan Reservoir on 15th May 1970.

154 BLACK-TAILED GODWIT *Limosa limosa*

Regular spring and autumn passage migrant in small numbers, with occasional birds remaining during summer and winter. Passage records extend over a wider range of dates than those of the Whimbrel, with the dominant passage season varying unpredictably from year to year. Since 1967, more birds have been recorded in autumn than spring in five years, and more in spring than autumn in four. Since numbers in spring are on the whole more stable, this may indicate that the heaviness of autumn passage reflects the breeding success of this species in Iceland, the area from which the majority of Gwent birds must come. Larger recorded numbers include 40 at Redwick on 1st May 1973, 28 at Undy in April 1971, 25 at Peterstone Wentlooge on 20th August 1974 and 22 at St. Brides on 30th March 1975, though most records refer to only small numbers of birds. Inland sightings include one at Abergavenny on 2nd May 1967, two at Garnlydan Reservoir on 3rd May 1969 and again on 18th July at the same site.

Many of the spring and autumn birds are in various stages of development or loss of the breeding plumage, some of these birds being non-breeders since they stay all summer. A few birds remain during the winter, e.g. two seen at Undy on 3rd December 1967 and three at Uskmouth on 3rd January 1968.

155 BAR-TAILED GODWIT *Limosa lapponica*

Regular spring and autumn passage migrant with small numbers remaining throughout the year. Between 1933 and 1963 there was only one record of this species, yet during the last ten years numbers have increased to such an extent that it is now recorded much more often than the Black-tailed Godwit. The autumn passage is heavier than the spring, with maxima from both seasons of 120 at Undy in September 1966, 100 in May 1971 and 60 on 2nd April 1974. Numbers at Peterstone Wentlooge are usually quite small but 50 were recorded on 6th May 1963. 1967 produced the first observations of wintering birds since 1933, with seven at Undy and singles at Goldcliff and Peterstone, all in December. 11 were present at Undy in December 1973 and 8 in January 1974. A few non-breeding birds, mostly juveniles, remain along the coast in summer with varying amounts of summer plumage. Many of the spring passage records are also of birds in partial summer plumage and some are observed starting to moult the primary feathers — a sure sign that they are non-breeders, though they may still spend the summer elsewhere. The Bar-tailed Godwit is very much a maritime species and there are no inland records from Gwent.

156 GREEN SANDPIPER *Tringa ochropus*

Predominantly an autumn passage migrant in small but regular numbers; also recorded during spring and winter. August, September and October are the months when this species is most likely to be seen, though it has been recorded in all months of the year including two or three in most winters. It is usually encountered at the inland reservoirs, along rivers and in the numerous fresh-water reens on the coastal levels. The Usk at Llanvihangel Gobion is a regular haunt with eight in July 1975 and seven in July 1974; eight were also recorded at nearby Llanover on 23rd April 1967. These are the largest numbers recorded, most other records refer to only one or two birds. Llandegfedd Reservoir has a regular small passage and birds often overwinter there. Four birds have been recorded at Abergavenny sewage works on two occasions — 21st September 1968 and 10th November 1969.

157 WOOD SANDPIPER *Tringa glareola*

Rare autumn passage migrant. Of the total of 13 records, four are from inland areas, with singles on the Usk at Abergavenny on 1st September 1972, at Abergavenny sewage works on 12th October 1968 and at Llandegfedd Reservoir on 8th September 1965 and 26th–27th August 1969. The remainder are from near the coast, mostly from fresh-water ponds and reens, such as those at Peterstone Wentlooge, Undy and Severn Tunnel Junction. These records, all of single birds, cover the period 23rd June to 12th October and are thus entirely restricted to the autumn passage period, though the June record is a little early. The main breeding range of this species is from Scandinavia eastwards, but a few pairs breed in northern Britain.

159 COMMON SANDPIPER *Actitis hypoleucos*

Regular breeder and passage migrant, occasionally remaining to overwinter. Breeding has been recorded along the rivers Usk, Trothy, Honddu, Monnow and their tributaries, as well as at Llandegfedd, Garnlydan, Carno and Cwm Tyleri reservoirs.

Autumn is the dominant passage period with maxima of 23 on 13th July 1968 and 18 on 15th July 1973, both at Peterstone Wentlooge, 16 in August 1966 at Llandegfedd Reservoir, a total of 20 at Ynysyfro Reservoir in autumn 1975 and nine at Undy in early July 1972. Records of birds inland in winter have come from the Usk at Abergavenny (1974), Llanwenarth (1968 and 1969), Llandegfedd (1974) and Ynysyfro (1970). It has also been seen in winter along the coast with 25 on the banks of the Usk at Newport on 7th November 1968, 10 at the same site on 30th December 1967 and six at Undy on 6th December 1970. Passage birds probably consist of continental as well as British breeding individuals.

161 REDSHANK *Tringa totanus*

Breeding resident in moderate numbers; passage migrant and winter visitor in larger numbers. Breeding has been confirmed widely over the coastal levels. Ingram and Salmon (1939) also mention breeding at a site near Abergavenny. Four separate families of chicks seen near Undy in 1974 are the nearest approach to a count of breeding pairs, though to judge from the number of territorial birds along the coastal plains in spring, the breeding population is possibly as large as 40 pairs.

The British breeding population is a distinct race of the Redshank, *T.t.britannica*, but winter visitors and passage migrants include the races *T.t.robusta* which breeds in Iceland and Faeroes, and *T.t.totanus* which breeds throughout continental Europe. The maximum number of wintering birds along the whole coast of Gwent was 691 recorded in November 1974, of which 660 were at Undy. The maximum at Peterstone was 130 in April 1975. Autumn passage is well marked in July and August, with peaks of 400 on 13th August 1969 at Undy and 90 in August 1974 at Peterstone. The spring passage is less clear cut, as it often coincides with the departure of overwintering birds and is thus not reflected in regular monthly counts.

The Redshank is a regular visitor inland at all times of the year, with peaks at Llandegfedd Reservoir of nine on 16th December 1973 and 14 at Abergavenny sewage works on 13th April 1969. It has been recorded at almost all inland waters, more commonly during spring and autumn than winter. Some records of birds during summer may indicate possible additional breeding areas, e.g. a pair at Ynysyfro Reservoir during 1970. Nocturnal passage during spring has been recorded in at least three years at Abergavenny.

162 **SPOTTED REDSHANK** *Tringa erythropus*

Passage migrant, mainly in autumn; occasional winter visitor. At one time this was a rare straggler to the west coast during migration (Humphreys, 1963), but it is now a regular autumn visitor and has also been recorded during winter and spring. About 130 birds have been seen in the county, principally during the autumn migration (July–November), with most birds occurring on the coast during August and September. Only six birds have been observed in spring, two at Undy on 5th May 1973, and singles at Llandegfedd Reservoir on 29th March 1969, Peterstone Wentlooge on 12th April 1974, and Undy on 12th and 27th April 1974. The two May birds were in summer plumage, as were three at Peterstone Wentlooge on 11th June 1975 and two at Newport Docks on 28th June 1970. The latter record, together with another six from June probably involve non-breeding birds. Winter sightings include singles on 24th December 1970, January 1971 and 24th February 1974 at Undy. As with several other species the increasing number of wintering birds probably reflects the series of mild winters experienced since 1963. The largest numbers seen have been seven on two dates in August and September 1969 at Undy. There are only seven inland records, five from Llandegfedd Reservoir and two from Garnlydan Reservoir.

165 GREENSHANK *Tringa nebularia*

Regular passage migrant in small numbers, mainly in autumn, especially August and September. Inland and coastal records are almost equally numerous for this species. Peak counts have come from Uskmouth ash ponds with 36 on 2nd September and 11 on 27th August 1973, from Undy with 20 on 14th September 1963 and 10 on 13th August 1969, and from Peterstone Wentlooge with 11 in September 1970. No other records have reached double figures. Inland, maxima of six were recorded at Llandegfedd Reservoir on 16th August 1972, three at Pant-yr-eos Reservoir during 27th August – 16th September 1972, and three at Wentwood Reservoir during 21st October – 23rd November 1970, as well as singles at most other inland ponds and reservoirs. Spring records occur from late March to mid-May, but are uncommon and usually involve only one or two birds, the earliest being one at Llandegfedd on 26th March 1968.

Small numbers winter in south-west Britain, and not surprisingly there are a few such records from Gwent — one at Peterstone on 22nd December 1966 and singles at Wentwood Reservoir during 24th November – 13th December 1971 and during 11th November – 24th December 1972.

169 KNOT *Calidris canutus*

Abundant winter visitor ; passage migrant in smaller numbers. A considerable amount is known about this species in Europe, mainly as a result of intensive ringing studies. The majority of British wintering Knot are Greenlandic and Canadian in origin. In autumn, at the end of each breeding season, these birds return to the North Sea estuaries to moult, later moving westwards across the country, like several other species, to winter in the estuaries around the Irish Sea. A large number remain behind in the east, but in hard winters these too may drift westwards. Thus the Knot in the Severn estuary do not reach peak numbers until November or even December in some years, and they depart quite suddenly in March and April. They are at the same time highly gregarious and mobile, and the bulk of wintering birds are concentrated in only a handful of very large flocks which roam freely over most of the estuary. Such large flocks have thus been recorded at most sites on the Gwent coast, including Peterstone Wentlooge, St. Brides Wentlooge, Newport Docks, Uskmouth, Goldcliff and Undy. Most observations are of 3–5,000 birds though over 10,000 were recorded at Peterstone on 13th February 1969 and at Undy in December 1973. Despite this tendency to concentrate in large flocks, small groups of a few dozen birds also occur at most sites in winter.

The autumn passage is very light, while in spring a few hundred birds are recorded, some in summer plumage. A few non-breeding birds remain throughout the summer, for example, a flock of 18 caught at Undy on 25th May 1974 consisted of nearly all juvenile birds, some in partial summer plumage and most starting to moult their primary feathers.

Inland records are uncommon for this species, but a single bird was seen on 27th April at Llandegfedd Reservoir in full breeding plumage, and 13 in flight between Rassau and Garnlydan on 26th February 1969.

170 PURPLE SANDPIPER *Calidris maritima*

Rare winter visitor and passage migrant with only nine county records. The comparative lack of records is undoubtedly due to the absence of suitable feeding areas for this species which prefers rocky shores. Three sightings have occurred in May, the others in September, October, November and December. All have been from the coast, five at Undy and four at Peterstone Wentlooge. With the exception of a pair at Undy on 6th May 1971, all records are of single birds.

171 LITTLE STINT *Calidris minuta*

Uncommon spring and autumn passage migrant with just over 70 birds recorded. Although only 15 birds have occurred during spring (3rd March – 7th May) they have included some quite large groups, for example, five on 2nd May 1969 at Peterstone Wentlooge and four on 3rd March 1932 at St. Brides Wentlooge. The remainder of the 44 county records, mostly singles, have occurred between July and November, especially in August and September and have often included immature birds. The most favoured spot is Peterstone Gout, but Little Stints have also been recorded from Sluice Farm, St. Brides, Uskmouth, Goldcliff, Undy and Black Rock. There have only been three inland records, one at Wentwood Reservoir on 5th October 1969, one at Llandegfedd Reservoir from 29th August to 3rd September 1972 and one at a slurry pond at Duffryn Farm, Llanvapley, in mid-September 1972.

176 PECTORAL SANDPIPER *Calidris melanotos*

The only record of this, the commonest transatlantic vagrant to Britain, was of a single bird at Peterstone Wentlooge on 17th September 1963.

178 DUNLIN *Calidris alpina*

Abundant winter visitor and passage migrant; a few pairs breed irregularly. This species bred on moorland in the north of the county in 1973, this being the first record for many years, though it was once seen regularly on the hills near Abergavenny. Song flighting of three birds was observed near Beaufort on 20th May 1971, only a few miles from a known breeding site in Breconshire. It is sufficiently elusive during the breeding season to have been overlooked in one or two other areas.

The breeders belong to the race *C.a.schinzii*, whilst the winter visitors, which are a little larger and are the most abundant wader in the county, belong to the nominate race *C.a.alpina.* This race arrives in the Severn estuary during October and November after moulting further east.

Dunlin utilize the whole of the muddy foreshore of Gwent from Peterstone Great Wharf to the Severn Bridge. Peak numbers are reached during the coldest part of the winter, with a maximum during March 1973 of 21,100 birds. Some individuals drift north and west again in early spring, but others remain to moult into summer plumage before doing so. During April and May, there is a considerable passage of birds heading for breeding areas in Iceland (*C.a.schinzii*) and north-east Greenland (*C.a.arctica*). The Severn is an important refuelling area for these migrants, which deposit fat rapidly during their brief stay. Since birds are arriving and departing almost continually during this period it is difficult to assess the numbers involved. Peak counts of about 10,000 have been obtained in several years, though the total number of spring passage migrants must be two or three times as great. These migrants winter in southern Europe and Africa. One of the Dunlin ringed at Collister Pill in May was re-trapped the following winter in Mauritania on the west coast of Africa. A few birds remain throughout the summer. The autumn passage during August and September is much less marked and involves only two or three thousand birds.

Inland records are most frequent during the spring and autumn passage, the maximum counts being 30 at Garnlydan Reservoir on 11th May 1970 and 12 at Llandegfedd Reservoir on 19th April 1966. The maximum number inland in winter was seven in December 1973, also at Llandegfedd.

179 CURLEW SANDPIPER *Calidris ferruginea*

Uncommon spring and autumn passage migrant. Until 1971 there were only 16 records of this species, all of them in autumn, but since that year there have been ten spring records (11th April – 26th June) and 16 autumn ones (1st August – 4th October). It is difficult to be sure that this represents a real change in status, for Curlew Sandpipers can easily go undetected in large Dunlin flocks. The spring records have been of only small numbers, usually singles, with a maximum of six on 24th May 1971 at Undy. Larger numbers have occurred in autumn, particularly September, e.g. ten at Undy on 21st September 1975, eight at Uskmouth on 22nd September 1967, five at Peterstone Wentlooge on 17th September 1967 and six at Undy in August 1975. There are only five inland records, all from reservoirs and three of them in one year; these are of single birds at Llandegfedd on 29th August and 13th September 1969, at Ynysyfro from 30th August to 2nd September 1975 and at Garnlydan on 31st August 1975, and of two birds, again at Ynysyfro, on 9th September 1975.

181 SANDERLING *Calidris alba*

Uncommon but regular spring and autumn passage migrant; recorded annually in numbers usually less than 20. The muddy nature of the intertidal zone in Gwent presents few opportunities for this basically sand-loving species and consequently there is no regular wintering population. Odd individuals do turn up in winter, however, such as the singles at Peterstone Wentlooge on 16th January 1952 and Undy on 13th February 1967. It occurs mainly in spring (1st April – 20th June) with a distinct peak in May; and also during autumn (July – 21st October) with a peak in September. The spring flocks often contain individuals in summer plumage. The migrants are well spread out along the shore and flock sizes are therefore small, but there have been fairly frequent records of flocks of up to about 30 from Uskmouth and Undy, with one of 50 at Undy on 30th August 1969. There are only two inland records, one from flooded fields at Llanellen on 14th May 1966 and one from Llandegfedd Reservoir on 12th May 1974.

184 RUFF *Philomachus pugnax*

Passage migrant, mainly in autumn. The passage has extended from 6th August to 29th October with most records in late August and early September. The species is equally common at Peterstone Wentlooge and Undy, the largest recorded groups consisting of seven on 30th August and again on 8th September 1974 at Undy. In addition there are six spring records of 12 birds between 27th March and 11th May, and four wintering records of single birds at Undy on 31st January 1971, at Peterstone on 22nd December 1966 and 6th January 1968, and at Uskmouth on 2nd February 1975. There is some evidence that this species is increasing in Gwent and in Britain as a whole. The only inland records are from Llandegfedd Reservoir: one on 21st August 1972 and two on 17th August 1975.

185 AVOCET *Recurvirostra avosetta*

Rare visitor with only six county records. In 1906 " a flock " was reported in the Severn and one was shot at Ynysyfro Reservoir in 1907. The next record was not until 1968 when one was seen from 4th to 6th April at Peterstone Wentlooge. The other records are of two in a reen near Bishton on 10th May 1969, one at Collister Pill on 20th June 1974 and two at Peterstone Wentlooge on 2nd August 1974. These records, restricted as they are to the passage periods, are most likely to be of birds from the more northerly parts of the breeding range in Europe, which winter in southern Europe and Africa. Part of the British breeding population moves to estuaries in the south-west, such as the Tamar, so that winter records are also a possibility for Gwent, though none have occurred so far.

187 GREY PHALAROPE *Phalaropus fulicarius*

Rare visitor on autumn passage with only six definite records. The earlier records are of single birds at Peterstone Wentlooge on 9th September 1933 and at Rogiet on 5th December 1954, while another bird seen at Peterstone on 18th September 1950 was very probably this species. More recently, sightings in October 1968 at Llandegfedd Reservoir on 7th and at Usk on 9th probably refer to the same bird, while another was seen at Llandegfedd on 29th November 1969. The most recent records are for September 1974, of single birds at Magor Pill from 4th to 9th and at Ynysyfro Reservoir on 9th. These occurred after a period of severe westerly gales; there were several other records from neighbouring counties at the same time.

188 RED-NECKED PHALAROPE *Phalaropus lobatus*

Only one record of a single bird. This individual was originally recorded as a Grey Phalarope, but later examination of photographs confirmed the opinion of some observers at the time that this was in fact a Red-necked Phalarope. The possibility of the existence of two birds, one of each species, is very unlikely but cannot be ruled out. The record came from a sludge pond at Lower House Farm, Coed Morgan, which was occupied from mid-November to late December 1972. This is particularly late for this species, which winters in the southern hemisphere.

189 STONE CURLEW *Burhinus oedicnemus*

Three records only. These are all of single birds at Undy on 10th April 1970, 11th November 1972 and 15th June 1973. Though this species breeds not far away in Dorset and winters in East Africa, it is only irregularly recorded on migration in Wales.

193 ARCTIC SKUA *Stercorarius parasiticus*

Rare and irregular passage migrant, usually in autumn. The first record is of an oiled bird, caught in exhausted condition, at Abergavenny in 1946 and it did not occur again until 1963, when a single was seen over fields at Peterstone Wentlooge on 19th October. Following a very probable sighting in 1967 (Pomarine Skua was not ruled out), dark-phase birds have been recorded in three of the last eight years: in 1968, one between Denny Island and the Gwent coast on 16th August; in 1972, two birds at Peterstone on 28th May, and in 1974, single birds, again at Peterstone, on 19th and 29th August. In addition, an immature skua, probably Arctic, was recorded on 21st August 1975 at Peterstone.

194 GREAT SKUA *Stercorarius skua*

Two records only. The first is of one harrying Arctic Terns at Peterstone Wentlooge on 21st September 1953 and the second of an exhausted bird at Redwick after several days of stormy weather in late March 1968. [Humphreys (1963) mentions a specimen in Newport Museum which, apparently, was shot at the mouth of the Usk, but no other details are given].

196 LONG-TAILED SKUA *Stercorarius longicaudus*

Two records only. In the last century one was shot at Rumney (Monmouthshire) in January 1892 and one flew down-channel past Goldcliff on 4th October 1970.

198 GREAT BLACK-BACKED GULL   *Larus marinus*

Breeding resident. It is reported at all times of the year throughout the county, usually in small numbers, but in recent years flocks of 15–30 have not been unusual, particularly on the coast in the autumn and winter.

There is a breeding colony on Denny Island. This began with a single pair in 1954, increased to 25 pairs by 1961, and since 1962 seems to have stabilised at between 30 and 40 pairs. During the breeding season small numbers of non-breeders, almost all immatures, are seen chiefly along the coast.

199 LESSER BLACK-BACKED GULL   *Larus fuscus*

Widespread and numerous at all seasons, breeds at one locality. The first breeding record came in 1969 with the discovery of about ten pairs nesting amongst a larger number of Herring Gulls on roof tops in and around Newport Docks. Despite the regular occupation of territories in several other districts, in such situations as the banks of the Usk and domestic roof tops, and the almost annual attempts to breed at Ebbw Vale Reservoir, Newport Docks has remained the only successful breeding site and in 1975 held nine pairs.

Outside the breeding season the species occurs throughout the county, particularly at reservoirs, rubbish tips and coastal sewage outfalls. During the winter, flocks generally contain fewer than 50 birds though up to 200 have sometimes been recorded in the period November–February at Undy and Llandegfedd Reservoir. From March to April numbers are swollen slightly by the arrival of passage migrants, and again from July to September when the increase is much more dramatic and flocks exceeding 100 have been recorded at Garnlydan Reservoir, and up to 520 at Llandegfedd.

The above data refer to the British race, *L.f.graellsii*. Records of individuals identified either as the Scandinavian race, *L.f.fuscus*, or the intermediate race, *L.f.intermedius*, are confined to 1975, when five birds were seen at Garndiffaith tip on 14th February, and one at Mardy on 29th June.

200 HERRING GULL   *Larus argentatus*

Common resident and winter visitor which breeds at several sites. A breeding colony has been known for many years on the Wye cliffs at Chepstow, but the number of nests on the Gwent side of the river has always been very small, e.g. two in 1968 and seven in 1975. There is also a colony on Denny Island which has existed at least since 1961 when eight nests were noted and subsequently held 38 in 1962, 120 in 1969 and *c*84 in 1974. Roof-top nesting was not noted until 1969 when a total of about 100 pairs was estimated on buildings in or around Newport Docks. This colony, which had no doubt been overlooked for several years previously, has remained stable in recent years and at the last count, in 1975, held 70 nests. Recently established colonies are at Livox Quarries: four nests in 1973, 12 in 1975; and in a railway cutting south-west of Chepstow: seven nests in 1975.

Immature, non-breeding birds are also present during the summer, and from autumn to spring, numbers are augmented by the arrival of immigrants. In winter, it is widely distributed and flocks of several hundred are commonly reported from favoured localities, particularly rubbish tips. The main winter roost is at Llandegfedd Reservoir which holds up to about 1,500, but many birds which feed in the county make regular flights to roosts on the islands of Flat Holm and Steep Holm.

201 **COMMON GULL** *Larus canus*

Autumn to spring visitor in moderate numbers, some remain through the summer. Although 25 were at Trelleck on 24th July 1972, autumn passage typically begins in August when small parties begin to arrive, particularly at reservoirs, and larger numbers are sometimes observed passing in southerly or south-westerly direction, as did a total of about 150 during 26th August 1967 at Monkswood. The main passage is most obvious on the coast where numbers in late autumn can be considerably in excess of those in winter, e.g. *c*400 in the Undy area in October 1972.

In winter it is less likely to be seen at rubbish tips than other gulls and is most often found feeding in fields, where flocks of over 100 are not unusual, and the largest ever recorded contained *c*650 birds near Usk in February 1972, and over 4,000 at Llandenny in January 1975. On the coast, winter numbers are generally low with few records reaching double figures. Llandegfedd Reservoir is the most regular roost and in some years holds as many as 200 birds. Roosting flocks are also reported, though less regularly, from Garnlydan and Wentwood Reservoirs where numbers have been as high as 150, and in 1975 a roost was found between Uskmouth and St. Brides Wentlooge which held at least 350 birds in February. It seems likely that most of the birds which feed in the county also roost within its boundaries, though in the winter of 1963–64 a daily flight-line was mapped which stretched from Hereford, through Abergavenny, Pontypool and Newport, and across the Severn to a roost at Avonmouth.

Wintering birds seem to leave mainly in March, but later in the spring (as in autumn) a distinct peak in numbers is often observed on the coast and presumably comprises birds which wintered further south. This peak has been as high as 300 at Undy in March 1972, while at Peterstone Wentlooge there were 160 in late April 1974 and 240 on 5th May 1975.

There are occasional records in the breeding season, all of immatures, and in 1974 up to four were regularly recorded at Peterstone throughout June and July.

202 GLAUCOUS GULL   *Larus hyperboreus*

One record only. A specimen shot at Marshfield on 10th March 1893 was later displayed in Newport Museum.

205 MEDITERRANEAN GULL   *Larus melanocephalus*

One record only; two adults in full summer plumage were at Peterstone Wentlooge on 3rd April 1975. In recent years this species has been recorded with increasing frequency in the neighbouring counties of Somerset and S. and W. Glamorgan.

207 LITTLE GULL   *Larus minutus*

Spring to autumn visitor in recent years only. Single birds at Llandegfedd Reservoir on 16th August 1972 and at Peterstone Wentlooge on 29th–30th June 1973 constituted the first and second county records respectively. In the spring of 1974 there was a remarkable influx which brought small numbers to Llandegfedd Reservoir on most days during 4th–29th May, with a peak of twelve on the 12th, and involving a total of about 22 birds. Sightings continued during the year with a party of eleven at Peterstone on 30th June, two and one respectively at Llandegfedd on 16th and 28th August, and three flying down the Usk at Caerleon on 24th September. In 1975, one was recorded at Peterstone on 23rd April and two on 7th May. Available information suggests that of the grand total of about 42 birds recorded in the county, over 75% have been immature.

This increase in records, which in neighbouring counties was observed some years earlier, reflects the expansion of the non-breeding range and seasonal movements of the species into much of Britain which has been occurring over the past decade.

208 BLACK-HEADED GULL   *Larus ridibundus*

Common non-breeding resident and autumn to spring visitor. Throughout the year it is widely distributed and favoured inland localities include reservoirs, sewage works, rubbish tips and flooded or freshly ploughed fields.

Although Gwent is the only Welsh county in which this species has not been known to breed, substantial numbers are present during the breeding season, particularly on the coast. For example, in at least the last three years (1973–75) a flock of 100–150 has been present at Peterstone Wentlooge throughout May and June. A few of these birds have been apparent full adults, but most have been immatures.

Numbers increase rapidly from July onwards, e.g. at Peterstone in 1974: 15th June, 130; 7th July, 400; 31st July, 520; 18th August, 850; while in the same year at neighbouring St. Brides Wentlooge a mixed roost of about 3,000 gulls, the bulk of which was this species, was present

Plate 7. LLANDEGFEDD RESERVOIR photographed in 1965, soon after its completion. The distance from the dam to the far shore is just over 2km (1.3 miles).

Keri Williams   *Plate 8.* LITTLE OWL WITH YOUNG. This species did not breed in Gwent until 1914 but is now widespread in most low-land regions

on 15th August. The mid-summer influx is also reflected in the large flocks, usually of several hundreds, which are seen hawking flying ants in the Newport vicinity at this season in most years. In 1972, on the coast east of the Usk estuary, a flock of about 3,000 had built up as early as late July which increased to 10,000 in August and dropped to 8,000 in September.

In winter, the Llandegfedd Reservoir population is usually in the range 2,000–3,000 from December to February and, as well as the more frequent flocks of several hundred birds, concentrations of up to 3,000 are not uncommonly found elsewhere, both inland and on the coast. A simultaneous count of all coastal regions on 13th February 1974 yielded a total of 17,000, and if this is added to other counts made on similar dates, of 1,000 at both Llandegfedd and Monmouth rubbish tip, and 3,000 in flooded fields at Llandenny, a total of 22,400 is obtained, which must still be a conservative estimate of the total present in the county at the time. The much smaller figures (4–5,000) obtained from co-ordinated roost counts made at dusk in January and February 1975, coupled with the observed departure at these times of large numbers of birds across the Bristol Channel, suggests that a high proportion of those which feed in the county during the winter, roost outside its boundaries. Wintering birds begin to leave in early March and by about mid-April only the summer population remains.

211 KITTIWAKE *Rissa tridactyla*

Rare visitor. There have been only six records, the first concerning a single bird at Newport Docks on 25th February 1928 and the next not until 1st June 1960 when another was seen at the mouth of the Rhymney (Monmouthshire). In recent years, a party of three was observed flying close inshore at Peterstone Wentlooge on 6th January 1968 after severe westerly gales, and single birds have occurred three times in autumn: offshore at Magor Pill on 13th October 1973, at Goldcliff on 6th October 1974, and at Peterstone on 21st August 1975.

212 BLACK TERN *Chlidonias niger*

Regular passage migrant in spring and autumn. A total of about 150 birds has been recorded, 31 of these irregularly from 1898 to 1957 and the remaining 119 since 1967. It is much commoner in autumn than in spring and the monthly distribution is: April, 3; May, 21; July, 1; August, 53; September, 61; October, 11. In spring, records have been confined almost exclusively to the short period 30th April–12th May with one as early as 22nd April, while in the autumn, the bulk has occurred between 16th August and 7th October, but exceptionally as early as 29th July and as late as 24th October. Although it has been recorded in each of the past nine years, annual totals have fluctuated greatly from about 77 and 26 respectively in 1970 and 1974 to less than five in each of the other seven years.

The favoured localities are inland waters, particularly Llandegfedd Reservoir, where since 1967 as many as 103 have been recorded. Elsewhere during this period there have been eight at Garnlydan Reservoir, one at Ynysyfro Reservoir and four on the coast. Records have most often referred to only one or two birds, but at Llandegfedd there were flocks of 36 in August and 20 in September 1970 and eight and nine respectively in the same months of 1974, while at Garnlydan there was a party of eight in May 1970.

217 **COMMON TERN** *Sterna hirundo*

218 **ARCTIC TERN** *Sterna paradisaea*

Regular passage migrants in spring and autumn. Owing to the difficulties associated with their identification in the field, most records of these species are indeterminate and, consequently, the two must be considered together.

Prior to 1951 there were about four records of each species and no more until 1966. Since 1966 a total of about 313 birds has been recorded which have a monthly distribution of: April, 34; May, 93; June, 8; July, 10; August, 58; September, 90; October, 20. Occasional birds have been as early, or late, as 14th April and 22nd October respectively, but in spring the vast majority have occurred between 22nd April and 4th May, and in autumn from 12th August to 7th October. The bulk of records are from Llandegfedd Reservoir and the coast generally, which together account for 291 birds, the remaining 23 being from other inland localities, particularly Ynysyfro Reservoir. The distribution between Llandegfedd and the coast varies significantly with the season; of the 135 birds seen in the period April–June slightly more than half have been on the coast, whereas of the 178 birds seen during July–October about 83% have been at Llandegfedd or other inland sites. Yearly totals have fluctuated enormously, with one and two respectively for 1972 and 1966 contrasting sharply with 46 for 1969 and an exceptional 126 for 1974. Flock-size has generally been less than ten, but parties of 17–31 have been recorded on four occasions, twice each at Llandegfedd and on the coast at Peterstone Wentlooge.

Of the total of 313 birds, 45 have been positively identified as Common and 46 as Arctic. Owing to their smallness, these figures are almost certainly unreliable as an indication of the relative abundance of the two species, e.g. the total for Arctic rests largely on a single flock of 30 at Llandegfedd in May 1974. Another source of error may be the bias toward inland waters where, for obvious reasons, the bulk of positive identifications (more than 5 out of 6) have been made

222 LITTLE TERN *Sterna albifrons*

Scarce spring and autumn passage migrant. Although it was said to have occurred on migration in earlier years, the first documented record is of birds seen at three places on the Wye on 7th June 1938 (Humphreys, 1963). The next occurrence was not until 1970 when two were seen at Llandegfedd Reservoir on 17th May. Subsequently, the species has been recorded in four out of five years: one over the Usk on 28th September 1972; another flying over the sea-wall at Peterstone Wentlooge on 5th May 1973; in 1974, single birds over the Usk at Llantrisant and at Llandegfedd, both on 18th May, and two flying offshore at Goldcliff on 8th September; and in 1975, one offshore at Peterstone on 18th May.

223 SANDWICH TERN *Sterna sandvicensis*

Spring and autumn passage migrant in small numbers. Following a very probable sighting at Undy in 1966, the first definite records were of single birds flying between Denny Island and the Gwent coast on 26th and 27th August 1967. Single birds at Undy on 27th and 28th April of the following year were the first spring records, while two which flew up-river as far as Usk bridge on 25th April 1969 were the first observed inland. In 1970, two were seen at Undy on 18th August and in 1971 a single bird at Peterstone Wentlooge on 11th July. The most recent records comprise: in 1974, two at Undy on 27th August, and a single, followed shortly by a party of ten, which on 15th September flew from directly inland to Peterstone Pill and passed out over the Bristol Channel in a southerly direction; and in 1975, two at Peterstone on 19th June and one at Llandegfedd Reservoir on 20th September.

224 RAZORBILL *Alca torda*

Three records only. Ingram and Salmon (1939) mention an occurrence at Portskewett before 1900. The only other records are from 1970, when single birds were seen swimming offshore at Goldcliff on 30th August and at Peterstone Wentlooge on 20th September.

This species, and to a lesser extent the Guillemot, are seen annually in small numbers at the Somerset localities of Sand Point, Brean Down and Steep Holm and in many years also at Lavernock Point (S.Glamorgan) where they have usually been flying up-channel. The surprising rarity of Gwent records for these species may be attributable, at least in part, to the absence of a vantage point comparable to those mentioned above, either for elevation, or protrusion into the Bristol Channel.

226 LITTLE AUK *Alle alle*

Three records only. One was shot at Magor in the winter of 1912 and another, which was picked up at Risca on 18th December 1968, flew off strongly when released at Goldcliff the following day. A bird found exhausted near Llanthony on 24th March 1975 died soon after and was deposited in the National Museum of Wales.

227 GUILLEMOT *Uria aalge*

Rare visitor. Records from the first half of this century refer to a single in winter plumage shot at Peterstone Wentlooge on 24th September 1935, and oiled birds picked up at Redwick (date unknown) and below Rhymney in 1940. More recently, a single seen at Undy on 21st January 1973 was found dead six days later, and birds identified as probably this species (Razorbill not ruled out) flew down the Usk at Abergavenny on 6th November 1971 and down-channel off Peterstone on 8th July 1975. (See comments under Razorbill: 224).

230 PUFFIN *Fratercula arctica*

The only record is of a juvenile which was picked up, exhausted, at Cefntilla Court on 17th October 1965.

232 STOCK DOVE *Columba oenas*

Fairly common breeding resident. It was recorded by Ingram and Salmon (1939) as breeding sparsely in central, northern and north-eastern districts, where it occupied such situations as cliffs in the Wye valley or hills, hollow trees and ruined buildings. Since then there appears to have been little change; breeding still occurs regularly, but at low density, in all districts except the south-west. In recent years it has appeared most common in the vicinity of Monmouth where nine breeding pairs were reported in 1973.

Small flocks may be seen from autumn to spring in any part of the county, usually of less than about 40 birds, though 300 were recorded at Llanover in March 1972.

234 WOODPIGEON *Columba palumbus*

Abundant breeding resident and winter visitor. It is widely distributed and breeds wherever there are trees. The arrival of winter visitors increases numbers, and from October to March flocks of up to 500 are common-place. A flock of c1,000 in an oakwood near the Sugar Loaf in November 1969 was exceptionally large. Movements of large numbers are occasionally noted, e.g. totals of over 1,000 passed westwards over Pontypool on several mornings during the last week of November 1970.

COLLARED DOVE *Streptopelia decaocto*

Common breeding resident. It was first recorded at Bassaleg in 1961. During the next eight years numbers increased rapidly, breeding records were received from many districts, and in some localities, e.g. Abergavenny, Usk and Newport, rapidly expanding colonies were founded. The rate of expansion of these early colonies is typified by that at Usk, which was started by a solitary pair in 1967, in the following year comprised seven pairs and in 1969 had increased to about 30 pairs.

It has now become established as a common resident which breeds throughout the county and in recent winters has congregated into flocks containing up to 150 birds.

235 TURTLE DOVE *Streptopelia turtur*

Summer visitor which breeds regularly, but sparsely, in all districts except the extreme south-west. The number of confirmed breeding records in any one year has never exceeded eight. In 1963 it appeared to be in decline (Humphreys, 1963), but since then numbers have seemed fairly stable and very recently may even have increased slightly. However, as with other not very numerous summer visitors, the numbers arriving fluctuate greatly from year to year and long term trends are difficult to see.

Spring passage is in some years noted as early as mid-April, but more usually from early to mid-May and with records seldom referring to more than two birds. In contrast to neighbouring S. Glamorgan, passage is more marked in the autumn, particularly on the coast at Undy, where flocks of ten or more birds have been seen in several years during July or August and stragglers have occurred as late as 11th October.

237 CUCKOO *Cuculus canorus*

Breeding summer visitor; fairly common and widely distributed in rural areas. The earliest arrivals are usually noted during the second week of April, occasionally earlier or later, but it is not widely recorded until near the end of the month. Most appear to depart during August or earlier and only a few stragglers are recorded in September.

241 BARN OWL *Tyto alba*

Breeding resident. It is frequently reported from all rural regions of the county, though less so from the coalfield valleys, and is nowhere very common. Over the last ten years the population appears to have remained fairly stable with breeding records received in almost every year, generally of one or two pairs, but four in 1972. British birds all belong to the race *T.a.alba*. A specimen of the dark-breasted race *T.a.guttata*, which breeds in northern Europe, was shot at Blaenavon in 1908.

244 SNOWY OWL *Nyctea scandiaca*

Two records only. One was reported at Bishton on 23rd December 1953 and another was said to have been seen in the vicinity of Cross Ash during the winter of 1915–16.

246 LITTLE OWL *Athene noctua*

Breeding resident. Formerly of doubtful occurrence in the British Isles, this species was successfully introduced into southern England during the latter half of the 19th century. Until 1914 it remained no more than a vagrant to Welsh counties and the only Monmouthshire record was of a single caught near Chepstow on 5th December 1901. During the first World War there was an influx northward and westward into Wales, and Monmouthshire was one of the first counties to be colonised. Breeding first occurred at Chepstow in 1914 and again at an unspecified locality in 1915 (Matheson, 1932).

Subsequently, it has become established as a widespread and fairly common resident with six to ten breeding records received in most years. Although some of these are from the western coalfield (e.g. Cwm Tyleri 1973) and the coastal levels (e.g. Peterstone Wentlooge 1968), the bulk are from the central area of the county.

247 TAWNY OWL *Strix aluco*

Fairly common breeding resident, widely distributed in rural, suburban and urban areas. Since 1967 the number of breeding records received each year has varied between seven and eleven, apart from 1971 when it was as high as 15.

248 LONG-EARED OWL *Asio otus*

Very scarce, has bred and may still do so. There are only three definite records from the early part of this century; two from around 1900 which refer to breeding near Chepstow and Abergavenny respectively, and the third to a bird shot near Usk in October 1926. There are no further records until 1967, since when, singles have been reported during the breeding season in most years, from a number of localities which would appear to offer suitable habitat for breeding.

249 SHORT-EARED OWL *Asio flammeus*

Autumn to spring visitor. It has for many years been known as an irregular winter visitor, chiefly to the coastal levels, and usually with no more than single birds involved. Since 1965, its visits to the county have been almost annual with records in eight out of eleven winters. Reports have generally been confined to the period September–March, though in 1971 at least one bird stayed on in the Magor area until 18th April, and exceptionally, one was seen at Oakdale on 20th July 1967.

The numbers of this species wintering in particular areas are known to be related to the local population of its principal prey, the short-tailed field vole, and large influxes can occur in years of high vole numbers. Small influxes have been observed in Gwent in four winters. The first was in 1938–39 and the remainder, all very recent, were in 1970–71, 1972–73 and 1973–74, when between four and eight birds were present in the coastal strip between Rogiet and Peterstone Wentlooge over a period of some weeks.

A bird ringed as a nestling in Norfolk in May 1973 was recovered at Peterstone in September of the same year.

252 NIGHTJAR *Caprimulgus europaeus*

Summer visitor in small numbers; breeds locally. Although described by Humphreys (1963) as uncommon, there has been an increase in records since about 1965, probably due to increased observation. It is usually associated with forestry plantations when they are at a stage of growth which affords cover but still gives some open space. Wentwood has provided this type of habitat for some years and there have been regular reports from this area, with up to eight pairs in 1970, but with a decline of numbers since then. There have also been regular reports, of usually not more than three birds, from Bassaleg, Cwmcarn Forest, the Blorenge and the Sugar Loaf, and isolated reports from elsewhere. Birds usually arrive in mid-May, the earliest being on 7th May 1971 at Wentwood; most depart again during August, though records in September are not uncommon.

255 SWIFT *Apus apus*

Common breeding summer visitor. In spite of the loss of some breeding sites due to redevelopment, the Swift remains a widespread breeding species. Early arrivals are seen in April, but the main flocks usually arrive during the first week of May and appear to travel up the river valleys before dispersal. Thereafter they exploit every area in which there is food, often flying low over the mountain pastures. Most birds have left again by mid-August, although there are September records in many years, with the latest on 5th October 1966, of five birds seen at Griffithstown.

258 KINGFISHER *Alcedo atthis*

Breeding resident. After a good recovery from the severe mortality suffered in the hard winters of 1961–62 and 1962–63, it is now regularly reported from about 35 localities annually. These are mainly along the rivers and the Mon.–Brecon canal, but also from the reservoirs, and the reens of the coastal levels. Since 1968 there have also been regular reports from the area between Rogerstone and Crosskeys, and since 1973 reports from other areas in the industrial valleys, suggesting that it may be attempting to recolonise these areas. There have also been occasional records of birds fishing in tidal creeks along the coast.

261 HOOPOE *Upupa epops*

Rare summer and passage visitor. There are 14 records altogether, all but one of which refer to single birds. They occurred in 1934, 1942 and in ten of the 18 years 1958–1975, and have a monthly distribution of: April, 2; May, 4; June, 3; July, 1; August, 2; September, 1; October, 1. The records are well scattered over all of the county except the north and west.

262 GREEN WOODPECKER *Picus viridis*

Breeding resident. After the heavy losses of the hard winter of 1962–63 it had recovered its former numbers by 1968, and in recent years has been regularly reported from over 40 areas. There are occasional sightings on the bare high ground in the north-west, and also from the relatively open areas of the coastal levels.

263 GREAT SPOTTED WOODPECKER *Dendrocopos major*

Breeding resident. It appears to have been less affected than the Green Woodpecker by the hard winter of 1962–63 and is now only slightly less numerous, with reports from about 30 localities annually. These are well spread over the county, being scarce only in the western valleys. Reports from some areas have suggested it is locally more numerous than the Green Woodpecker: e.g. at Llanarth and Glascoed in 1968 and in the lower Usk valley in 1969.

264 LESSER SPOTTED WOODPECKER *Dendrocopos minor*

Breeding resident. Apart from occasional breeding records (never more than one a year) there are usually only isolated sightings, from about 15 localities annually, widely scattered through the county. The elusive behaviour of the species suggests that these very probably underrate its status.

265 WRYNECK *Jynx torquilla*

Rare passage migrant, mainly in autumn. Ingram and Salmon (1939) quote four breeding records around 1900 and otherwise describe it as an uncommon but probably regular spring passage migrant. In the past 25 years there have been only two spring sightings, both near Newport, in March 1955 and in March 1973, and one in early summer at Wentwood in June 1965. All other recent records are in the period July–September, and involve single sightings in 1964 and 1965 and six altogether between 1970 and 1974.

271 WOODLARK *Lullula arborea*

Very scarce breeding resident. Humphreys (1963) describes it as an uncommon breeding resident, with small flocks on the coast in winter. In recent years breeding has only been confirmed in 1967 and 1974, and suspected in 1971, from the same site at an altitude of 300m (1000 ft.) in the west of the county; there are no other breeding records since about 1930. Apart from parties of 11 at Wentwood in June 1968 and nine at Abergavenny sewage works in December 1967, there are only four other records since 1965, all referring to one or two birds.

272 SKYLARK *Alauda arvensis*

Common breeding resident. Although most numerous on the hills, it is seen and heard widely throughout the county, breeding in most areas.

Some movement is regularly noted on autumn migration watches, though usually only in small numbers; a total of over 500 at Goldcliff on 19th October 1968 and a flock of 350 over Peterstone on 11th October 1975 were exceptional. Hard-weather movements are also recorded occasionally, a notable instance being 4,000 near Abergavenny in February 1969.

273 SHORE LARK *Eremophila alpestris*

One record only, of two birds seen on the foreshore near the Rhymney estuary (Monmouthshire) on 2nd November 1972.

274 SWALLOW *Hirundo rustica*

Breeding summer visitor and passage migrant. It breeds widely throughout the county and is common everywhere below about 450 m (1,500 ft.).

First arrivals are generally in the first week of April, occasionally in March, but large parties are not usually seen until late in this month or early in May; for example, 250 at Llandegfedd Reservoir on 26th April 1968 and 1,000 there on 5th May 1973. On autumn passage large numbers may occur at any time from the last week of August to the first week of October, usually at reservoirs and along the coast. The larger numbers recorded include 4,000 on telegraph wires around Goldcliff on 27th August 1968, 2,000 passing Undy on 14th September 1969, 2,500 at Llandegfedd on 25th August 1970, and 1,200 passing Peterstone Wentlooge on 2nd October 1973. Autumn 1975 was notable for the lack of large flocks seen and may represent the start of a long-term trend. Records are usually very scarce in the second half of October and rare in November, the latest being on the 5th of this month.

An albino was seen at Abersychan on 8th September 1968.

276 HOUSE MARTIN *Delichon urbica*

Breeding summer visitor and passage migrant. It breeds throughout the county where there are suitable sites; the largest colonies reported have been at Caerleon, Llanthony Priory, and Kings Fee, Monmouth and have held 65, 40 and 20 nests respectively.

Its movements tend to coincide with or overlap those of the Swallow, though in both spring and autumn, the passage peak is usually a little later. The largest numbers recorded have been 4,000 passing Peterstone Wentlooge on 18th September 1968 and 2,000 passing Llandegfedd Reservoir on 15th September 1971, while parties of up to about 200 are fairly common. Late October records are more usual than for the Swallow but there have been only two in November, the later on the 17th.

Two albinos in the same nest were reported in 1974.

277 SAND MARTIN *Riparia riparia*

Breeding summer visitor and passage migrant. As a breeding species it is locally common along suitable stretches of rivers, particularly the

Usk, Monnow and Wye, and it seems certain that its numbers were underestimated by Humphreys (1963). The most extensive enquiry into its breeding status remains that conducted in 1965 along the Usk. This disclosed a total of about 1,500 nests on the Monmouthshire section of the river, with the largest colony containing 210 holes (Rogers and Gault, 1968). Since 1965, there has undoubtedly been some decline. For example, the colony at Rockfield which held 120 holes in 1969 had only 48 in 1975 and fewer than 25 in some of the intervening years. However, the decline seems to have been less severe than in neighbouring Glamorgan (Salmon, 1974) and in 1975 there were still thriving colonies on the Usk, two of which had 90 and 60 holes respectively. In 1968, summer floods on the Usk washed out 50–60% of nests at a time when second broods would have been hatched and led to an estimated loss of some 3,000 unfledged young on this river alone (Sarson, 1969).

The Sand Martin is one of the first migrants to arrive and records in early or mid-March are not unusual. In spring and particularly autumn, migrating flocks are commonly seen but these have suffered a very great decline in recent years, with the result that flocks of 1,000 at Llandegfedd Reservoir on 1st May 1968 and coastal movements of up to 2,000 in that year have never subsequently been approached in size. Since 1971, the number seen on any one occasion has not exceeded 100. September records are scarce, there are only two for October and the latest occurred on 1st November 1969.

278 **GOLDEN ORIOLE** *Oriolus oriolus*

Rare summer visitor. Records include single birds at Abergavenny on 8th September 1939, at Caerleon on 21st June 1942 and at Abercarn on 23rd April 1944. In recent years birds have been seen at Wentwood in 1967, 1969, 1970, 1974 and 1975, usually on several occasions during the summer, which has led to suspicions of breeding. A male was recorded singing at Marshfield on 10th June 1970.

279 **RAVEN** *Corvus corax*

Breeding resident. It nests widely in all parts of the county except the coastal levels, but most frequently in the hills of the north and west; nesting sites on both cliffs and trees are used. It is often seen in flocks over mountains and near rubbish tips, and outside the breeding season in coastal districts and occasionally along the shore. In recent years, flocks of 20–30 and occasionally up to 50 birds have not been unusual.

Forty years ago it was much rarer and Ingram and Salmon (1939) described it as breeding only in the extreme north and north-west corners of the county, with probably no more than one or two regularly occupied sites. This situation stemmed largely from its persecution by game-preserving interests and as these declined the county was recolonised, probably mainly from southern Powys where it had always remained numerous.

280/1 CARRION/HOODED CROW *Corvus corone*

The Carrion Crow *C.c.corone* is a common and widespread breeding resident. It is most numerous in the vicinity of towns and on the coastal levels, and is least so on the hills in the north. In autumn and winter, large flocks, often of 100–150 birds and occasionally of over 200 are regularly recorded in situations where food is plentiful, particularly at rubbish tips. Complete or partial albinos are fairly frequent.

The Hooded Crow *C.c.cornix* is a rare visitor, mainly in autumn. There have been nine records since 1925, all of single birds and from widely scattered localities. Of these, three have been in October, three in November, one in February and two in March. One of the March records concerns a bird which was apparently mated to a Carrion Crow at Bettws Newydd in 1953.

282 ROOK *Corvus frugilegus*

Breeding resident. It is common throughout most of the county, except for the coastal levels where there are few rookeries and also on the very high ground. The results of the National Rook Survey in 1945 showed 96 rookeries within the county with a total of 5,625 nests, giving an average rookery size of 58 nests. A similar survey in 1975 revealed 160 rookeries but with a total of only 2,770 nests, giving an average rookery size of 17 nests. In the 1975 survey all but six of the rookery sites were below about 220 m (700 ft.); a wide variety of trees was used, ash and beech being the most popular, and one rookery was sited in pylons.

Rooks are often seen in flocks, mainly outside the breeding season, often of up to 100 and occasionally of as many as 500. Movements to and from roosts in numbers of this order have also been recorded, notably of 700 at Glascoed in 1970 and of 500 over Monmouth in 1973.

283 JACKDAW *Corvus monedula*

Breeding resident. It is common throughout the county and breeds in nearly all districts, the usual sites being hollow trees, chimneys and unworked quarries. Flocks of up to 200 birds are regularly seen, often at rubbish tips, while movements to and from roosts, often of several hundred birds and frequently mixed with Rooks have been noted. The principal roosts have been those at Clytha, Monmouth, and near Pant-yr-eos.

There are two records of partial albinos in recent years.

284 MAGPIE *Pica pica*

Common breeding resident. Since the early 1940s it has extended its range of habitats and is now commonly seen in rural as well as sub-urban areas. Although most often seen in ones and twos, flocks of up to 30 are regularly reported from many areas, mainly in winter.

285 **NUTCRACKER** *Nucifraga caryocatactes*

Two records only, of single birds seen in St. Julian's Wood, Newport on 19th October 1954 and near Llanhilleth on 12th November 1968; the latter coincided with an invasion of Britain by large numbers of birds of the Siberian race *N.c.macrorhynchus*. [Humphreys (1963) also mentions two doubtful records from the 19th century.]

286 **JAY** *Garrulus glandarius*

Breeding resident. It is widely seen in woodlands throughout the county, though usually only in ones and twos, but occasionally in parties of 10–15 in winter.

In 1975 there was some evidence of a substantial movement into the county in late September, with widespread records of parties of up to ten birds during October. The species is subject to irruptions from the continent and it is possible that these records represent part of such an irruption. Ingram and Salmon (1939) cite another such instance in October 1923 when a large flock was seen at St. Mellons and smaller flocks elsewhere.

287 **CHOUGH** *Pyrrhocorax pyrrhocorax*

Rare visitor. The only recent record, and the most reliable, is of one seen at Abergavenny sewage works on 30th September and 1st October 1972.

[Ingram and Salmon (1939) quote three records between about 1880 and 1905, and state that it was said to have nested on the Skirrid Fawr in about 1880, while Humphreys (1963) adds two other unconfirmed reports for 1959, and classes all these as doubtful occurrences.]

288 **GREAT TIT** *Parus major*

Common resident; breeds widely. It is found breeding in a wide variety of situations including natural holes and nestboxes, and in all regions of the county up to about 450 m (1,500 ft.). It had recovered from the severe winter of 1962–63 by the summer of 1965 and since then the sum of the average populations in all four C.B.C. plots is 37 pairs in a total of 220 hectares (542 acres). Recorded winter flocks have not exceeded ten birds.

289 **BLUE TIT** *Parus caeruleus*

Common resident; breeds widely. Its distribution is very similar to that of the previous species, but evidence from the C.B.C. plots suggests that it is about twice as numerous; on average, the nestbox colonies also support about two pairs of Blue Tits for every pair of Great Tits. Flocks of up to, and sometimes over 50 birds are not unusual in autumn and winter, and small numbers are sometimes seen feeding among *Spartina* heads on the shore. There is evidence of some southerly movement in autumn, when parties have been seen flying in this direction from the coast (e.g. *c*30 due S. at Goldcliff on 14th September 1974), but the only evidence of a return movement in spring involves the recovery, on 27th March 1975, of a bird which had been ringed 19 days earlier in Bridgwater (Som.).

290 **COAL TIT** *Parus ater*

Breeding resident. It is regularly recorded in all districts except the coastal levels, but is nowhere very numerous. The sum of the average populations on the C.B.C. plots is seven pairs in a total of 220 hectares (542 acres), which is only about one fifth and one tenth, respectively, of the numbers of Great and Blue Tits. In common with both of the latter species its numbers declined during the severe winter of 1962–63, but had recovered by the summer of 1965. In winter, flocks of up to ten birds are not unusual but one of 36 in Wentwood in January 1974 was most exceptional.

292 **MARSH TIT** *Parus palustris*

Breeding resident. Like the previous species, it is widely but thinly distributed in all districts except the coastal levels, and also similarly, the sum of the average populations on the C.B.C. plots is seven pairs. In most, but not all years fewer records are received than of Coal Tit and this probably reflects a slightly less numerous status. Unlike other tits, this species seemed to suffer little reduction in numbers during the winter of 1962–63.

293 **WILLOW TIT** *Parus montanus*

Breeding resident. It was not recorded in the county until 1942 but had almost certainly been overlooked in previous years owing to its resemblance to the Marsh Tit. It is widely but thinly distributed, and like the previous two species is seldom recorded on the coastal levels. The sum of the average populations on the C.B.C. plots is only two pairs; in most years fewer records are received than of Marsh Tit but it may still be overlooked to some extent. Winter flocks of up to seven birds are occasionally recorded.

294 **LONG-TAILED TIT** *Aegithalos caudatus*

Resident, breeding in all districts and most numerous in agricultural areas. The sum of the average populations on the C.B.C. plots is eight pairs which suggests a status similar to that of Coal and Marsh Tit. By contrast, the larger number of records received annually suggests that it is appreciably more common than either of these species, but may in reality merely reflect the ease with which it can be recognised and its tendency to congregate into winter flocks of about 20, 30 or occasionally 40 birds. Its susceptibility to hard winters is well known, but in Gwent, the 1962–63 winter seemed to affect it less than those of 1939–40 or 1946–47.

295 BEARDED TIT *Panurus biarmicus*

Three records only. The first was in 1966 when up to three birds were seen on several occasions from January to March in a reed-bed at Newport Docks. The second was in October 1971 when a party of 14 was seen at Minnetts Wood. In December 1974, a male and two females were seen at Uskmouth.

296 NUTHATCH *Sitta europaea*

Fairly common breeding resident. It appears to be most numerous in the eastern part of the county where there is a greater abundance of suitable woodland. Up to about ten breeding records have been received annually since the mid-1960s and apart from a possible decline in 1969 a fairly stable population has been indicated.

298 TREECREEPER *Certhia familiaris*

Fairly common breeding resident. It is widespread and occurs in both wooded and agricultural areas. Following the severe winter of 1962–63 it was absent entirely from some localities but it had reappeared by the summer of 1964 and was present in normal numbers by the summer of 1965.

299 WREN *Troglodytes troglodytes*

Abundant breeding resident. Although it was almost wiped out in the winter of 1962–63, its numbers recovered rapidly during the following years and at the Wern Farm census plot had increased four times by the summer of 1965 and six times by 1967. Since then, its numbers have remained stable and the sum of the average populations on the four C.B.C. plots is about 110 pairs in a total of 220 hectares (542 acres). It is one of the commonest birds in the county and also one of the most widespread with a habitat range extending from the sea-wall right through to rocky hilltops.

There are records of communal winter roosting in natural and artificial House Martins' nests.

300 DIPPER *Cinclus cinclus*

Breeding resident, locally frequent. Although most numerous in the north and north-west it is widespread as a breeding species and occurs on most fast-flowing rivers and streams where the water is shallow and unpolluted. In recent years, records from the western industrialised valleys have become more frequent and this trend may continue if pollution levels continue to drop. The average annual number of breeding records from 1972 to 1975 is about fifteen.

301 **MISTLE THRUSH** *Turdus viscivorus*

Breeding resident. It is widespread and frequent as a breeding species, generally less common than the Song Thrush though in some localities possibly more common. Although it is more numerous in the lowlands it also breeds in the higher valleys around the hill farms. It showed a higher mortality than either Song Thrush or Blackbird in the severe winter of 1946–47; there is little information for 1962–63 but in neighbouring Glamorgan it seemed to suffer less in that winter.

It is seen in flocks, usually of up to about 30 birds, and mainly in autumn and winter, though parties of 50 have been recorded twice in June and July. The largest flock recorded was of about 400 at Penpergwm in February 1973. There is one record of an albino.

302 **FIELDFARE** *Turdus pilaris*

Regular winter visitor, sometimes in very large numbers. Apart from an exceptional record of ten at Cwmbran on 20th August 1974 the earliest recorded arrivals have been in early September, on the 7th at Upper Cwmbran in 1972 and on the 14th at Fforest Coal Pit in 1974. The main influx is usually in October. Most leave the county again during March though stragglers occur until the third week of April, and in 1974, one was recorded as late as 7th May. Winter flocks vary in size from about 50 up to 5,000 birds, usually mixed with Redwings. There is some evidence that flock sizes may generally be smaller in mild winters. Hard-weather movements are recorded and are usually associated with snowfall. There is one report of an albino in 1968.

303 **SONG THRUSH** *Turdus philomelos*

Common breeding resident. It is widely distributed within the county, but as with other common birds, it is under-reported and the only indications of its numbers and their fluctuations tend to be the figures from the Common Birds Census. These have indicated a very stable population since the early 1960s and the sum of the average numbers of breeding pairs on the four C.B.C. plots is 36 in 220 hectares (542 acres).

The frequency of this species relative to the Blackbird is of con-siderable interest. Heathcote, Griffin and Salmon (1967) point out that the ratio of Song Thrushes to Blackbirds in the Wild Gardens, Roath Park, Cardiff in the breeding season of 1910 was 4:1, whereas in 1967 the ratio was reversed. In Gwent, a 4:1 numerical superiority of the Blackbird was apparent in a survey of an area of farmland in 1946 and 1947, and has also been indicated more recently by the C.B.C. figures.

In recent years, small flocks of about 25 birds have been recorded in autumn and winter and presumably comprise winter immigrants. There is a single record of partial albinism (white collar and flecked wing-coverts).

117

304 **REDWING** *Turdus iliacus*

Common winter visitor. There are a few records of arrivals in the third week of September but the main influx occurs in October, a striking example being 3,500 birds which were observed on an early morning watch at Goldcliff on 19th October 1968. Most birds leave again in March, though stragglers commonly occur during early April and the two latest records were on 27th April 1966 at Pandy and on 8th June 1969 at Llanellen.

During the winter, it occurs widely, though mainly on the lower ground and often in company with Fieldfares. Flocks of several hundred birds are frequent and of up to 5,000 occasional. In an exceptional movement during anti-cyclonic weather in February 1968, about 12,000 were reported landing on the levels between St. Brides and Peterstone Wentlooge. Song and sub-song have been heard from February to April.

307 **RING OUZEL** *Turdus torquatus*

Breeding summer visitor. It is one of the earlier migrants to arrive and first sightings are generally in early April, though occasionally in the last week of March. Most birds depart during late summer, and September records, though fairly regular, are few.

As a breeding species it is sparsely distributed in the wilder hill districts of the north and north-west but also breeds irregularly on high ground in the south of the coalfield, for example, at Risca in 1968, Wattsville in 1971 and Mynyddislwyn in 1974. Its numbers seem to have been steadily decreasing since 1970 but no really reliable figures are available. Records at lower altitudes are very few and are generally of passage birds in spring and autumn.

308 **BLACKBIRD** *Turdus merula*

Breeding resident. It is abundant and widespread, being about four times as common as the Song Thrush (q.v.) and extending further into the hills and higher. The sum of the average populations on the four C.B.C. plots is 120 pairs in a total of 220 hectares (542 acres). Following a severe reduction in numbers during the winter of 1962–63 the figures for the Wern Farm area reveal a steady increase from then until 1967, after which there was a slight decline to a lower but stable level.

Evidence for the influx of some birds during the winter is provided by the recovery on 29th January 1932 of a bird which had been ringed in Denmark on 17th June 1929. Small flocks of up to about 20 birds which occur on the coastal levels in winter may be of similar origin.

Plumage variations recorded include full and partial albinos together with birds showing various combinations of golden-brown, grey, buff and orange-tan.

Plate 9. RAVEN AT THE NEST. There are few cliff sites in Gwent and nesting in trees occurs commonly. The inner lining of wool can be seen in this photograph.

Keri Williams   *Plate 10.* FEMALE REDSTART carrying food for the young. At least three items can be seen — a spider, a beetle larva and a geometrid moth caterpillar.

311 **WHEATEAR** *Oenanthe oenanthe*

Breeding summer visitor and passage migrant. Its breeding strong-holds are the mountainous areas of the north and west. In 1965 it was described as numerous in these areas and there are no indications of any change in status. The earliest arrival dates, for inland as well as coastal areas, are in the third week in March and the latest departure dates usually in the third week of October, although in 1969 one was seen at Undy on 5th November. Flocks of up to 46 have been reported in coastal areas on autumn passage and there is a late April record of 25 at Llandegfedd Reservoir.

Although Humphreys (1963) describes the Greenland or " Greater " Wheatear *O.o.leucorrhoa* as being seen regularly on both spring and autumn passage, he quotes records of two only, which were at Peterstone Wentlooge on 11th October 1951 and 3rd April 1952; the only subsequent record of birds showing the characteristics of this race concerns two at Goldcliff on 29th August 1970.

317 **STONECHAT** *Saxicola torquata*

Breeding resident and winter visitor. In most recent years there have been only isolated breeding records, mainly from the southern areas, and it is doubtful whether these accurately reflect its status. In 1975 however, there were six confirmed breeding records, nearly all in the hills of the north-west.

In winter, numbers are increased by immigrants and reports are widely scattered but most numerous along the coast. About 26 were seen in the Peterstone Wentlooge area in the autumn of 1975, which is an unusually large number and may have represented passage movement. Otherwise, birds along the coast are usually seen in scattered ones or twos, and in most winters the total present on the levels is probably around 30.

318 **WHINCHAT** *Saxicola rubetra*

Breeding summer visitor. It is fairly common in the hills of the north and west, and an indication of its density is given by reports from St. Mary's Vale of 14 pairs in 1974 and at least seven pairs in 1975. Humphreys (1963) also mentions the coastal levels and waste ground inland as regular breeding habitats; however, apart from an isolated instance in 1971 there have been no recent records of breeding on the coastal levels and very few elsewhere away from the hills.

Both arrival and departure dates have been irregular in recent years but the normal times would appear to be late April and the end of September respectively. There have been two March records, the earlier being on 17th March 1973, and last records of the year have twice been in late October. Two November records and two others on 6th December 1970 and 3rd January 1966 indicate the possibility of birds over-wintering.

320 **REDSTART** *Phoenicurus phoenicurus*

Breeding summer visitor. Humphreys (1963) described it as fairly common and breeding locally, mainly in the central areas and the hills of the north. In recent years there has been some decline in numbers, with few breeding records (about ten annually) mainly scattered over the same areas. There have also been recent reports of complete absence from areas where it was formerly well established, for instance, near Usk in 1975. The local decline reflects the national trend of a substantial drop in numbers as shown by the Common Birds Census results (Sharrock, 1976). Because of its specialised habitat requirements of mainly open areas with mature trees, the clearance of the latter may well be an important factor in the species' decline.

Spring passage is normally first noted in mid-April with widely scattered sightings of ones and twos. Autumn passage records are again mainly of small numbers but occasionally of parties of up to 10, and are most numerous on the coast. The latest records are usually towards the end of September; there is one later record, of one at Malpas on 17th October 1975.

321 **BLACK REDSTART** *Phoenicurus ochruros*

Rare winter visitor and passage migrant. There are two records from the 1930s and 14 more in six of the nine years 1967 to 1975, all of which concern single birds. 12 records are of sightings in the winter months, October to February, with three from April to May (two of which, in April 1974, almost certainly concern the same bird) and one in August. Three of the records are of birds at inland sites (Abergavenny, Monmouth and Trelleck); the rest refer to the area around Newport and the coastal levels. The increase of records in recent years suggests that the species may have been often overlooked in the past.

322 **NIGHTINGALE** *Luscinia megarhynchos*

Rare summer visitor; has bred. It was formerly described by Humphreys (1963) as not uncommon in the Wye valley and Raglan areas, but at present Gwent lies just outside its regular breeding range, which has contracted slowly but steadily for many years (Sharrock, 1976). There are only two recent breeding records, both from an area in the east of the county (probable in 1970, confirmed in 1975). Other records are of birds singing, sometimes for up to two weeks, and nearly all in the south-eastern half of the county; the only exceptions were at Risca in 1961 and near Tredegar in 1971. There is one early record of a bird seen and heard at Bulmore on 30th March 1970; all other records are from late April to June.

325 **ROBIN** *Erithacus rubecula*

Breeding resident. It is widespread and abundant in all lowland areas and even breeds sparsely in the uplands. Although its numbers were considerably reduced in the hard winter of 1962–63, perhaps by as much as 50%, it had apparently recovered by 1964. Since then its numbers have remained very stable and the sum of the average populations on the C.B.C. plots is 82 pairs in a total of 220 hectares (542 acres).

Nocturnal song has been increasingly noted in the last four years, though so far only in artificially lit areas.

327 GRASSHOPPER WARBLER *Locustella naevia*

Breeding summer visitor. Since Humphreys (1963) described it as a very local breeder, there appears to have been an increase in numbers from 1967 to 1971, and a steady decline since then. The species now appears to be largely dependent on young forestry plantations and the decline may be attributable to their growth to too great a height and density. The largest numbers of singing birds reported in breeding areas have been 18 in the Little Oak area of Wentwood and nine near Bassaleg, both in 1972; by comparison, the 1975 figures for the same areas were three and two respectively.

Spring passage is usually first noted in the third week of April and into May; there was an unusually large passage concentration of 22 singing at Magor Reserve on 4th May 1969. After the cessation of song in July, autumn passage goes virtually unnoticed; the only later records are both from 1968, of one found dead near Garnlydan on 2nd August and three seen at Magor Reserve on 2nd September.

333 REED WARBLER *Acrocephalus scirpaceus*

Breeding summer visitor. It is an uncommon but fairly regular visitor, mainly to areas on the coastal levels, notably Newport Docks, Magor Reserve and the Wentlooge area. In the 1960s its main stronghold was at Newport Docks, where July totals of over 50 and 41 were reported in 1964 and 1967 respectively, and 20 were heard singing in May 1966. More recently, records have been more widespread, with a greater number of reports from the Wentlooge area, but rarely of more than three birds at any one site.

There are few records of either spring or autumn passage, but these suggest that arrival in early May and departure in mid-September is the normal pattern. There is one exceptionally early record of a single bird at Magor Reserve on 7th March 1965, while the latest record is on 22nd September 1975.

334 MARSH WARBLER *Acrocephalus palustris*

Two records of this rare summer visitor. Two birds were seen at Undy on 15th August 1964 and five young were successfully reared in the south of the county in 1972. The latter appears to be the first definite breeding record for Wales (Hope Jones and Davis, 1973).

337 SEDGE WARBLER *Acrocephalus schoenobaenus*

Breeding summer visitor. Humphreys (1963) described it as a not uncommon summer visitor breeding regularly in suitable locations, most numerous among the reeds of the coastal levels and locally distributed along the river valleys. This remained the situation, though probably with some annual fluctuations, until 1972, when there was a general impression of a reduction in numbers. This has continued and constitutes a local reflection of the overall national decline evident from the returns of the Common Birds Census (Batten, 1973; Batten and Marchant, 1975; Batten and Marchant, 1976). However, the 1975 records for Gwent are suggestive of a partial recovery.

Although it has been seen as early as 25th March in 1965, the main passage seems to occur in the last week of April. Most autumn passage records occur in the second and third week of September, with the latest on 4th October 1973.

339 MELODIOUS WARBLER *Hippolais polyglotta*

Very rare passage migrant. There are only four records, all in the three-year period 1968–1970, of single birds on 12th August 1968 at Peterstone Wentlooge, on 2nd August 1969 at Goldcliff, and on 28th August 1970 at both Llandegfedd Reservoir and Glascoed Common.

343 BLACKCAP *Sylvia atricapilla*

Breeding summer visitor; small numbers over-winter. It is widespread and common and numbers have apparently been stable in recent years. This has generally been true in Britain overall, although a decline was reported in 1974 (Batten and Marchant, 1976). Humphreys (1963) remarked that there had been several recent instances of Blackcaps wintering in the county and this has become an annual occurrence since the winter of 1968–69. In 1969–70 reports indicated a wintering population of at least eight birds and this has not subsequently been equalled.

The presence of wintering birds makes it difficult to identify dates of arrival of genuine migrants, though there can be little doubt that the main arrival usually occurs during the first two weeks of April. There is a scarcity of September records suggesting that most have departed before this month.

346 GARDEN WARBLER *Sylvia borin*

Breeding summer visitor. It is fairly common and widely distributed. Like the Blackcap, it needs a fairly dense shrub-layer, but may be found wherever this occurs. Despite its rich and beautiful song it seems often overlooked owing to its skulking habits. National figures indicate that its numbers have remained relatively stable over the last ten years (Batten, 1973; Batten and Marchant, 1975a; Batten and Marchant, 1976) and there is no reason to suspect that the same has not applied in Gwent.

First sightings are generally from the second week of April onwards, though occasionally in March, the earliest being on 12th March 1969. August records are scarce and there are only two in September, the later being on the 28th.

347 WHITETHROAT *Sylvia communis*

Breeding summer visitor. Humphreys (1963) described the White-throat as a common summer visitor, second in numbers to the Willow Warbler and nesting everywhere in suitable habitats. It was the most common warbler of the thick hedgerows of the coastal areas. This situation obtained until 1969, when there was a catastrophic decline in numbers: it was thought possible that they were down to only one-third of the numbers for the previous year (Davis & Hope Jones 1969). It is as yet uncertain whether there has been any real subsequent recovery; national figures do not support one (Batten, 1973; Batten and Marchant, 1975a; Batten and Marchant, 1975b; Batten and Marchant, 1976). It has been suggested that the cause of this decline is the prolonged drought in their winter quarters, the Sahel Zone of West Africa (Winstanley, Spencer & Williamson, 1974).

Although there is one record for 6th April 1965, the main influx seems to come in the third and fourth weeks of April. Autumn passage records begin in late August, continue into September and have been as late as the 20th.

348 LESSER WHITETHROAT *Sylvia curruca*

Breeding summer visitor. It breeds rather locally in the county but is nevertheless fairly widespread. In contrast to the Whitethroat, national figures indicate an increase in numbers in recent years, at least until 1974 (Batten, 1973; Batten and Marchant, 1975a; Batten and Marchant, 1976) This trend has also been discernible in Gwent with reports reaching an all-time peak in 1974. There can be little doubt that this species is frequently overlooked.

Earliest arrivals are usually noted in the last week of April. Autumn passage records are frequent in August and occasional in September with one as late as the 20th.

354 WILLOW WARBLER *Phylloscopus trochilus*

Common breeding summer visitor. The most numerous and widely distributed of the warblers, it breeds throughout the county up to an elevation of 450–600m (1,500–2,000 ft.). Its numbers considerably exceed those of the Chiffchaff and the sum of the average populations on the four C.B.C. plots is 75 pairs in a total of 220 hectares (542 acres).

First arrivals are sometimes noted in the third week of March but more usually in the fourth, and it does not become widespread until mid-April. Autumn records occur frequently up to the end of October and one on 18th November 1970 was exceptionally late. In 1970, a single bird wintered at Upper Cwmbran.

356 CHIFFCHAFF *Phylloscopus collybita*

Breeding summer visitor. It is less common than the Willow Warbler and less widely distributed, being more dependent on high trees and woodland and absent from higher and wilder country of the north and west. Nevertheless, it is fairly common and breeds regularly in all wooded districts. The sum of the average populations on the four C.B.C. plots is 26 pairs in a total of 220 hectares (542 acres).

As has been noted in Glamorgan (Heathcote, Griffin and Salmon, 1967) the early spring records have tended to become progressively earlier and now occur in the first week of March, or even late February, although the main influx has remained in early or mid-April. Autumn passage records are frequent in September and often continue into the first half of October. Since the winter of 1967–68, records of wintering birds have been almost annual and are tending to increase in number; as with the Blackcap, this development makes it difficult to identify the dates of arrival and departure of genuine migrants.

357 WOOD WARBLER *Phylloscopus sibilatrix*

Breeding summer visitor. It is the least common of the *Phylloscopus* warblers breeding in Gwent. Nevertheless, it is locally fairly numerous, particularly in areas of sessile oak or mixed deciduous woodland on the hillsides. In spring it is usually recorded from the last week of April onwards. There are very few autumn passage records though they do include a party of as many as ten at Llandegfedd Reservoir on 7th August 1969. There are no September records but one was seen, again at Llandegfedd, on 10th October 1969.

364 GOLDCREST *Regulus regulus*

Resident breeding species and winter visitor. Its main stronghold remains the forestry plantations but it is encountered in all types and sizes of woodland, and up to considerable altitudes provided there are trees. Large flocks occur in winter which may contain immigrant birds. It suffered badly in the severe winter of 1962–63 and recovery has taken up to ten years. Latterly it has spread to garden hedges and shrubberies even in the most built-up areas. There are several records of birds feeding on the ground and at bird tables in winter.

365 FIRECREST *Regulus ignicapillus*

Mainly an irregular winter visitor, but recently a resident and probable breeder in one area. It was formerly very rare with only three records up to 1942; these were all of single birds, at Pontypool in 1926, Peterstone Wentlooge in February 1937 and Llandegfedd in January 1942.

Records in recent years began in 1972, with one at Henllys on 11th January and another at Mamhilad on 30th October and 1st November. In 1973 there was again one at Mamhilad on 16th October and two at nearby Goytre on the 19th. In 1974 there were four records, one at Abergavenny in January, one in Lasgarn Wood and another singing at Llandegfedd Reservoir in March, and one at Penhow in April. In 1975 there was one in Abergavenny on 18th January, while in May and June up to three were heard singing in Wentwood, where they probably bred. This appears to be the first such record for Wales, but in view of the recent expansion of its breeding range into southern England (Parslow, 1973) it seems likely that it could become established here in the near future.

366 **SPOTTED FLYCATCHER** *Muscicapa striata*

Summer visitor. It is fairly common and breeds widely, though records from the coastal strip most often refer to passage birds in August or September. First sightings have all been in the period 17th April – 14th May and the latest sightings generally during early or mid-September with one exceptionally late bird at Kilgwrrwg on 11th November 1973. Flocks are seldom seen and the largest recorded are of 12 birds at Lydart in June 1967 and 13 at Abertillery in September 1972.

368 **PIED FLYCATCHER** *Ficedula hypoleuca*

Summer visitor, fairly frequent locally. It was formerly regarded as rare and irregular, and Humphreys (1963) lists only 19 records between 1899 and 1962. Of these, nine were breeding records and all but four were later than 1942.

Its present status dates only from the mid-1960s and appears to be a direct consequence of the erection of nestboxes in suitable woodland which occurred during this period and is the subject of a separate chapter in this book. Since 1968, the total number of pairs breeding in nestboxes has remained fairly steady at between 18 and 26. Breeding records outside boxes have varied annually from nil to four, but with eight in 1975, which when added to the total in boxes gives a grand total of 30 for that year.

Earliest sightings have all been between 15th April and 11th May and the latest generally in the first week of September, though in 1973 one was seen feeding over the Monnow on 17th December. Passage records away from the breeding habitats in both spring and autumn have been remarkably scarce, with rarely more than two or three annually.

370 **RED-BREASTED FLYCATCHER** *Ficedula parva*

Three records only: a female was seen in a garden at Wentwood on 20th and 21st August 1969, a party of six or seven in Cleddon Wood, Trelleck on 14th July 1973, and a single male at Wentwood on 21st May 1975. This species was also recorded at Slimbridge (Glos.) in July 1973.

371 DUNNOCK *Prunella modularis*

Breeding resident. Widespread and abundant in all areas except the treeless uplands of the north and west where it is only occasionally found. It is not usually gregarious, but a party of nine was recorded in a garden at Caerleon in 1973. There is also a remarkable report of three birds having been killed by a Robin in a garden at Parc Seymour during one week in 1974.

373 MEADOW PIPIT *Anthus pratensis*

Breeding resident. It is common in the north and west where it is the dominant species on the high ground and frequently enters built-up areas and gardens. It breeds more sparsely along the coastal strip and is also found on open and waste land throughout the county.

In lowland areas numbers increase during winter and quite sizeable flocks are often recorded, for example, over 200 at Nash in January 1968. The tendency for lowland numbers to increase sharply after the onset of hard weather coupled with the much sparser population on the hills in winter, suggest that some of the winter increase in the lowlands represents merely a local movement from high to low ground. However, there is also a large passage of birds through the county in autumn which is particularly noticeable on the coast in the early morning, and it is likely that many of these remain to swell the winter population. Details of autumn movements along the coast are given in the separate chapter on migration, but about 300 per hour is quite usual on days from mid-September to late October. Spring passage movements have been noted twice with about 100 moving N.E. at Goldcliff on 30th March 1961 and a " large " number N.W. over Abergavenny on 4th April 1971.

374 RICHARD'S PIPIT *Anthus novaeseelandiae*

The only record is of one seen at Peterstone Wentlooge in company with a large flock of Meadow Pipits on 26th September 1951.

376 TREE PIPIT *Anthus trivialis*

Breeding summer visitor. It is fairly common and breeds in most parts of the county apart from the coastal levels and above the tree line on the hills. As elsewhere in Britain young forestry plantations have become important breeding habitats in recent years.

It is often overlooked, which makes changes in its status difficult to discern, but despite this there seems to have been a definite decline from 1969 with numbers remaining low until 1973. Since then, some recovery has been apparent and this has been particularly well documented in St. Mary's Vale, where numbers of breeding pairs have increased from possibly as few as five in 1973 to 21 in 1974 and 35 in 1975.

Since 1966, first sightings have all been in the short period 9th–19th April. In most years there are autumn passage records from the coast, usually of very small numbers, from late August to late September. However, about 30 were recorded at Undy on 17th September 1966 and 20 at Peterstone Wentlooge on 31st August 1968. The latest record is of eight at Ynysyfro Reservoir on 18th October 1969.

379 ROCK/WATER PIPIT *Anthus spinoletta*

The Rock Pipit *A.s.petrosus* is a scarce breeding resident and winter visitor. Humphreys (1963) described it as apparently breeding on Denny Island, but the only recent breeding record from this site was in 1969. Breeding has also been recorded along the coast at Peterstone Wentlooge in 1969 and possibly at Goldcliff in 1974.

From August to March it is distributed generally but very thinly along the coast and is most numerous from December onwards, when, in 1967 and 1968, reports suggested a total population of about 20 birds.

There are four records from well inland: single birds at Llanwenarth in January 1968, Abergavenny sewage works in February 1970 and Llanvihangel Gobion in August 1971; and two birds at Brynmawr in 1974.

The Water Pipit *A.s.spinoletta* is a winter visitor, fairly regular in recent years at one locality. Apart from three at Magor Pill on 27th September 1974 and single birds at Llandegfedd Reservoir on 8th November 1969 and 20th January 1974, all records have been from Abergavenny sewage works or its immediate vicinity in the period 1967–1974. At the sewage works itself there were records of up to two birds from November to February 1967–68, and from December to March 1968–69; up to nine from November to March 1969–70; up to three from December to January 1970–71; singles from November to December 1971, and singles in November 1972. In 1974 there were two birds at the nearby Castle Meadows on 25th April.

380 PIED/WHITE WAGTAIL *Motacilla alba*

The Pied Wagtail *M.a.yarrellii* is a breeding resident. It is very common in open country, particularly in the vicinity of buildings, both domestic and industrial and is renowned for its occasional choice of unusual nest sites such as on industrial machinery. It is least common on high ground where it tends to occur around farms.

In winter, its numbers are swollen by the arrival of immigrant flocks which often congregate into large roosts, the most notable being that at Nevill Hall Hospital, Abergavenny, which in 1974–75 and 1975–76 held up to 400 birds from November to January. Although movements along the coast are observed in autumn it is not usually one of the more numerous species recorded on organised watches, and a southward passage of 500 in two hours at Undy on 19th October 1963 was unusually large. A roost of 400 at Abergavenny sewage works on 12th October 1970 presumably comprised mainly passage birds.

The White Wagtail *M.a.alba* is a spring and autumn passage migrant. It is mostly recorded singly or in parties of fewer than ten, from mid-March to early May and again from late August to early October. Larger flocks have been recorded, notably 40 at Abergavenny sewage works on 13th September 1970 and 25 at Llandegfedd Reservoir on 15th September 1971. Birds showing the characteristics of this race have occasionally been recorded during the breeding season.

381 **GREY WAGTAIL** *Motacilla cinerea*

Breeding resident. It breeds commonly along water courses everywhere in the county apart from the coastal levels where it is much scarcer. It is also frequently encountered near static water tanks and reservoirs regardless of adjacent buildings or disturbance.

Numbers on the coastal levels show some increase in winter, probably as a result of local movement. The largest flocks are always recorded in March or April or from August to October and must reflect passage through the county; they usually contain no more than ten birds but a party of 19 was recorded at Llanyrafon on 9th September 1967.

382 **YELLOW/BLUE-HEADED WAGTAIL** *Motacilla flava*

The Yellow Wagtail *M.f.flavissima* is a breeding summer visitor, locally frequent, and a common passage migrant. Its status has changed little from that described by Humphreys (1963); it still breeds thinly but regularly along the coastal levels and more sporadically at locations further inland, particularly the Usk and Monnow valleys.

The annual total of recorded breeding pairs has usually been less than five but in 1974 this number was reported from Llandegfedd Reservoir alone, and the county total was eleven. Numbers were again higher than usual in 1975 with a total of eight pairs, of which only one was at Llandegfedd.

First sightings of the year have usually been during the second or third weeks of April, never before the 7th, and small flocks occasionally of as many as 20 birds continue to occur on the coast into early May. In autumn, flocks of 50 or more are not unusual during late August and early September, generally feeding on the coastal saltings and roosting among *Spartina* on the shore. Even larger numbers have been noted passing along the coast during early morning watches: in 1969, about 100 at Goldcliff on 23rd August and at Undy on 14th September; in 1974, about 100 at Goldcliff; and in 1968, 184 passed Goldcliff during a 20 minute period. There are occasional records during October, the latest of which concerns 24 birds at Kemeys Inferior on 15th October 1969.

The Blue-headed Wagtail *M.f. flava* is an occasional summer visitor and passage migrant, regular since 1972. A pair showing the characteristics of this race bred successfully at Llandegfedd Reservoir in 1974, rearing four young, and a second male was seen there on three dates during the breeding season.

There are nine other records, one from Pontnewydd and the remainder from the Wentlooge area. Apart from a pair in 1940, these comprise sightings of single birds in 1936 and annually since 1972, with a distribution of three in April, three in May, two in June and one in July.

In 1975, variant birds with mainly grey and white plumage were seen in the Wentlooge area on three occasions between 3rd May and 4th July. Two of these sightings are known to have referred to the same bird.

383   WAXWING   *Bombycilla garrulus*

Irregular winter visitor, almost annual in recent years. It was previously considered to be very rare and the only records prior to 1965 are of a bird shot at Magor in January 1914 and six at Risca throughout February 1947. Since 1965–66 it has occurred much more regularly with records in six out of the ten winters to 1974–75. The largest numbers occurred in 1965–66 when about 70 birds were recorded around Cwmbran and Newport throughout November and December, with parties of up to 19 being seen in January and February and ten flying over Newport on 30th March. Smaller numbers were seen during 1967–68 and 1969–70 with maxima of 20 birds in both winters, at Treworgan Common on 21st December and near the Skirrid on 1st November respectively. In both 1965–66 and 1967–68 there were large irruptions of the species to Britain. In the winters 1970–71, 1971–72 and 1973–74 there was a total of 14 records, all of small numbers usually during November and December, and at various localities including Abergavenny, Pant-yr-eos, Newport and Llandegfedd. The largest party was six at Cwmbran in December 1970. As in other parts of the country birds are most often recorded when they enter suburban gardens to feed on berry-bearing shrubs, particularly cotoneaster.

384   GREAT GREY SHRIKE   *Lanius excubitor*

Rare and irregular winter visitor. One was seen near Peterstone Wentlooge on 9th April 1933, two at Trelleck in April 1954 and another at Magor Reserve on 3rd January 1966. On 28th December 1970 one was heard singing near the Nedern Brook. Single birds have been recorded at Peterstone in each of the last three years: on 11th November 1973, 19th October 1974 and 8th December 1975; while at Llandegfedd Reservoir one was seen in the wood near the dam on 30th December 1975.

388   RED-BACKED SHRIKE   *Lanius collurio*

Rare summer visitor, formerly more common. In the past it was recorded as breeding near Marshfield, Newport, Portskewett, Llantarnam, Monmouth, Abergavenny and the Llanthony valley (Humphreys, 1963), while the Baker-Gabb collection includes eggs and nests from Abergavenny, five in 1889 and two in 1890 (both in the same field). In the 1940s a pair attempted unsuccessfully to breed near Maesglas in 1944 while another pair nested successfully at Llanfoist in 1944, 1945 and 1946. Single birds were also recorded at Trelleck in July 1952 and near Caldicot on 21st June 1958.

It was not recorded again until 1969 when a male was seen on 3rd September at Peterstone Wentlooge and a female on 20th September at Wentwood. Single birds were also recorded in August 1970 at Shirenewton, in June 1973 at Magor and between Bettws and Fforest Coalpit, and on 10th September 1974 in a Croesyceiliog garden.

389 STARLING *Sturnus vulgaris*

Very common breeding resident and winter visitor. It is widely distributed, breeding in rural, urban and industrial situations in all districts. Its numbers are greatly increased in autumn and winter by vast immigrant flocks.

Autumn and winter roosts containing thousands of birds are recorded from several localities, notably 20,000 at Goytre and 15,000 at Ebbw Vale in 1965, with a similar number at Newport Docks and Uskmouth Power Station in 1966, and the largest of all, 100,000 at Glascoed in 1973. It appears these roosts are gradually abandoned after a period and smaller ones are started, some of which may then grow into major ones.

Many of the birds feeding in Gwent in winter appear to use roosts in adjoining counties, such as those at Gilfach Goch (Mid-Glam.) (Humphreys, 1963), and the reed beds at Llangorse Lake (Powys).

390 ROSE-COLOURED STARLING *Sturnus roseus*

Three records only: a specimen in the National Museum of Wales was shot in 1836 near Magor, a female was shot at Monmouth on 11th September 1937, and one was seen at Llandenny on 16th April 1959.

391 HAWFINCH *Coccothraustes coccothraustes*

Very local breeding resident in small numbers. Humphreys (1963) indicates a similar status twenty years ago and describes it as most numerous in the Abergavenny, Monmouth and Chepstow districts. Recent records indicate that the Abergavenny district remains its main stronghold, with reports of breeding in three recent years and regular sightings in small numbers since 1970 suggesting a breeding population of about four pairs. Breeding was also confirmed near Abercarn in 1975 and strongly suspected near Monmouth in 1974 and 1975; the latter is the only other district where recent reports are more than sporadic. Other recent records, about two annually, comprise isolated sightings usually of only one or two birds; apart from single birds at Cwmavon and in the Grwyne Fawr, these are scattered over a strip of country from Pontypool to Chepstow.

392 GREENFINCH *Carduelis chloris*

Breeding resident. It is common throughout the county and breeds in all suburban and cultivated areas, though not in the hills. Flocks of up to 200 are occasionally reported in winter, mainly from the coastal levels and the Usk valley; the largest flock recorded is 300 at Monkswood in April 1970.

Some movement has been noted on autumn migration watches, though in small numbers compared to other finches; the largest numbers recorded have been 50 on three occasions, each in October.

393 GOLDFINCH *Carduelis carduelis*

Breeding resident. It had apparently increased considerably in the 1950s from its former numbers (Humphreys, 1963) but has shown no recent change, with widespread successful breeding over most of the county except the high hills. Flocks of up to 100 are commonly reported in winter, mainly from the low-lying areas; there was one exceptionally large flock of 500 at Peterstone Wentlooge in October 1964. Autumn movements of about 50 are regularly noted on migration watches; the largest recorded movements are 200 on 27th August 1968 and 150 on 10th October 1971, both at Goldcliff.

394 SISKIN *Carduelis spinus*

Mainly a winter visitor and in recent years a very local resident. It is now widely recorded in winter in parties of up to 50 and occasionally more: one exceptionally large flock of 250 was seen at Llantrisant in December 1975. In past years it has been most regularly reported feeding in waterside alders and also occasionally in birches, but since 1974 the reports have been more generally widespread.

The species has been extending its breeding range and is known to have bred recently in southern Powys. Although not yet proved to breed in Gwent, there are summer records which indicate this as a future possibility: a family party at Undy in August 1969, singing males in spring at Wentwood in 1971 and 1975 and at St. Brides Wentlooge and Pontypool in 1975, and a pair seen at Wentwood in July 1974.

395 LINNET *Acanthis cannabina*

Breeding resident, less numerous than in former years. It successfully occupies the whole county, its breeding range being limited only by the upper bush line on the hills. From late summer through autumn and winter it is frequently seen in flocks of up to 100 and occasionally more.

It is the most numerous finch observed on autumn migration watches, several hundreds being regularly seen, with the largest total over 2,000 at Goldcliff on 6th October 1968.

396 TWITE *Acanthis flavirostris*

Uncommon visitor in small numbers, mainly in autumn and winter. Before 1939 it was considered very rare with records only from Abergavenny and Llantarnam (Ingram and Salmon, 1939). Since 1965 there have been 13 records in all, occurring in seven of the eleven years 1965–1975. Of these, ten have been spread over the period 28th August – 2nd February, with two in April and one in June. The sightings have been widely scattered over most of the county except the north and east. In all cases numbers reported have been small, the largest parties being recorded in 1974: eight at Usk in November and six at Ebbw Vale in December.

397 REDPOLL *Acanthis flammea*

Local breeding resident and winter visitor. Ingram and Salmon (1939) mention breeding records from Newport, Llantarnam and some of the western valleys; there were no further reports of breeding until 1967 when it was suspected in the Cwmyoy area and at Wainfelin, and confirmed at Cwmyoy in 1969. In 1971 breeding colonies were reported in forestry plantations near Ebbw Vale and Tredegar, with 12 and 20 pairs respectively. From 1972 onwards several pairs were recorded in summer in and around Abergavenny and breeding here and at Llanfoist was confirmed in 1974 and 1975. Since 1974 there have also been summer records from Wentwood, Ynysyfro, Twmbarlwm, Bassaleg and western Newport.

The species is often seen in autumn and winter both in small parties and in flocks of up to 50, often mixed with other finches; larger flocks of up to 200 were frequently recorded in 1970 and 1971.

In 1967, two birds at Llanwenarth on 4th January and ten at Llanvaches on 11th February showed some of the characteristics of the northern race *A.f.flammea*; Ingram and Salmon (1939) also mention that birds of this race had been recorded in past winters, but without citing any instances.

401 BULLFINCH *Pyrrhula pyrrhula*

Breeding resident. It is fairly common and breeds in most areas except the hill country of the north and west. It is usually only found in scattered pairs or post-breeding family parties; the concentrations complained of by fruit growers in other counties have not been experienced here.

A bird of larger size and brighter colouring recorded in a Pontypool garden on 2nd February 1970 was thought to be of the northern race *P.p.pyrrhula*.

404 CROSSBILL *Loxia curvirostra*

Uncommon visitor and probably resident in small numbers; occasionally breeds. Up to 1930 there had only been about ten records, including reports of breeding from Newport in 1901 and near Abergavenny in 1909, and parties of ten seen at Cwmyoy in March and December 1910. Family parties were also recorded between Pontypool and Abergavenny in 1956 and at Llanarth in 1958.

The species has been recorded in every year since 1966, although with only one or two records annually until 1970. Since then records have been most regular in the Wentwood area, where it probably bred in 1971 and has frequently been seen in small parties, usually of less than ten, though 20 were recorded in July 1971 and July 1972. Reports from elsewhere are more varied; outstanding among these are confirmed breeding at Cwm Tyleri in 1972 and flocks of 40 at Clytha in November 1972 and 24 at Cwmcarn in April 1973. The remaining records are isolated sightings mainly of ones and twos, well scattered over the county, including two from the coast: one at Peterstone Wentlooge in December 1967 and two at Redwick in November 1969.

The increase in sightings in recent years suggests that the species may breed regularly in Gwent, but the extent and nature of the areas of apparently suitable habitat could make confirmation difficult.

407 **CHAFFINCH** *Fringilla coelebs*

Common breeding resident and winter visitor. It is one of the commonest birds in the county, found almost everywhere and breeding from the coast up to the bush line on the hills. Numbers are greatly inflated by winter immigration resulting in roving flocks, often of up to 250 birds, usually seen on agricultural land. Some movement is also regularly recorded on autumn migration watches in numbers of 100 or more, with the largest total recorded of over 1,000 at Goldcliff on 19th October 1968.

408 **BRAMBLING** *Fringilla montifringilla*

Regular winter visitor, usually in small numbers. Once it was considered rare, appearing only in hard weather (Humphreys, 1963). Although never common, it has been regularly recorded in recent years from October to March (and once on 1st April), usually in numbers up to about 20, and often among larger flocks of Chaffinches. There are also four records of substantial flocks of 100 birds or more, the largest being *c.*200 at Manmoel in February 1971 and again at Llantrisant in December 1973.

409 **YELLOWHAMMER** *Emberiza citrinella*

Fairly common breeding resident. It was always considered to be numerous and typical of any countryside area but in recent years there has been a marked decline in some districts and it is now more confined to the agricultural areas and the gorse- and bush-covered foothills. In winter it is recorded in flocks, often along the coast and usually containing fewer than 20 birds, though occasionally up to 200; exceptionally, about 400 fed for two weeks in December 1973 on a playing field at Pontllanfraith.

410 CORN BUNTING *Emberiza calandra*

Rare visitor, mainly in summer in recent years; has bred twice, at Pant-yr-eos in 1903 and near Llanvapley in 1970. It was formerly described as a rare visitor to coastal districts (Ingram and Salmon, 1939). In recent years there have been nine records, apart from the breeding record, in 1962 and in six of the eight years 1966 to 1973. Of these, six were in the period May – August with two in January and one in March; all referred to up to four birds only. Five of the sightings were in the coastal region between Undy and Chepstow, and the others at Peterstone Wentlooge, Risca, Ebbw Vale, and Llandegfedd Reservoir (a bird found dead).

415 CIRL BUNTING *Emberiza cirlus*

Rare visitor. Early in this century it was a very local resident, with breeding recorded at Abergavenny, Usk, Rogerstone and Newport and occasional reports from other districts up to 1925 (Ingram and Salmon, 1939). Since then there has been one breeding record, at Llanarth in 1968. The only other recent records are of one at Glascoed in May and June 1968, a male singing at Llanarth in 1969 and another seen at Magor on 27th June 1970.

416 ORTOLAN BUNTING *Emberiza hortulana*

The only record is of two birds observed on 24th June 1971 on a roadside wall on the Blorenge, one of which was identified as the male of this species.

421 REED BUNTING *Emberiza schoeniclus*

Locally common breeding resident. It is most numerous along the coastal levels and the river valleys, but it is found at all altitudes in suitable habitats. There is some indication of local movements in winter, with reports of birds in gardens and at bird tables; there is one remarkable record of 16 in a Newport garden in February 1971. Winter flocks of up to 50 are often seen along the coast, the largest number reported being up to 200 at Peterstone Wentlooge in October 1967.

422 LAPLAND BUNTING *Calcarius lapponicus*

The only record is of a single bird at Undy on 13th December 1970.

423 SNOW BUNTING *Plectrophenax nivalis*

Scarce winter visitor, mainly along the coast. The only inland records are from Abergavenny, of one shot in December 1890 and three seen in January 1968. The remainder comprise three between 1912 and 1930 (Ingram and Salmon, 1939) and about thirteen in recent years, in 1964 and seven of the nine years 1967 to 1975. These are spread over the winter months October – March, and all refer to birds seen on or close to the coast, with most at Undy and Peterstone Wentlooge. The largest numbers recorded are up to ten in March 1964 and up to eight in November 1967, both at Undy.

424 HOUSE SPARROW *Passer domesticus*

Very common breeding resident. Abundant near habitations and in all built-up areas, but mainly absent from the open high ground in the north and west, and apparently slow to colonise newly developed rural areas. Four melanistic birds were seen at Abergavenny throughout the summer of 1966, and there are frequent reports of albinistic birds.

In recent years an increasing tendency to make use of nestboxes and House Martin nests has been noted (Humphreys, 1975).

425 TREE SPARROW *Passer montanus*

Breeding resident. The decline recorded from 1930 to 1950 (Humphreys, 1963) has been reversed, and it is now fairly common in all areas apart from the industrial valleys. It is often seen in flocks, of up to 30 and occasionally up to 80, the largest being 200 at Newport rubbish tip on 27th December 1975. Some autumn passage movement is frequently observed during October, the largest number recorded being 130 in 1968.

As with the previous species there has been an increasing use of nestboxes in recent years. In both cases this may reflect a reduction in natural holes caused by the clearance of old orchards and trees.

DOUBTFUL OCCURRENCES

There are some species for which there is some doubt about the reliability of the only records of their occurrence in the county. For the following species, which are listed by Ingram and Salmon (1939), the doubt arises from their antiquity and lack of documentation; in most cases no details, other than those quoted below, are given.

37 **LITTLE BITTERN** *Ixobrychus minutus*
One was shot at Marshfield many years ago.

78 **BEAN GOOSE** *Anser fabalis*
One was shot from a flock of ten at Penpergwm on 27th December 1906.

97 **WHITE-TAILED EAGLE** *Haliaeetus albicilla*
An immature bird, locally obtained, was at Llanwern Park.

146 **GREAT SNIPE** *Gallinago media*
It was reputed to have occurred several times, but no definite records are given.

195 **POMARINE SKUA** *Stercorarius pomarinus*
One was shot near Pontypool on 31st October 1919.

386 **WOODCHAT SHRIKE** *Lanius senator*
One in the National Museum of Wales is labelled " Monmouthshire."

There are also six recent sightings which deserve a mention in this section. In each case, owing to some uncertainty on the part of the observers, the records refer to birds which were " very probably " the species indicated:

338 **AQUATIC WARBLER** *Acrocephalus paludicola*
One at Magor Reserve on 5th June 1965 and two at Peterstone Gout on 8th October 1972.

340 **ICTERINE WARBLER** *Hippolais icterina*
Single birds at Devauden on 20th July 1964 and at Llanarth on 23rd August 1966.

341 **OLIVACEOUS WARBLER** *Hippolais pallida*

One at Llanvaches on 25th April 1968.

406 **TWO-BARRED CROSSBILL** *Loxia leucoptera*

The only record is of a bird seen from 3rd to 5th October 1970 in company with Crossbills in larch trees at Goytre Wharf, which had conspicuous white wing bars and was thought to be of this species.

OUTSTANDING RECORDS FOR 1976

The following records all occurred in 1976, too late to be included in the main species section, and with the exception of Goosander fall into one of the following categories:— (i) species previously recorded on fewer than ten occasions; (ii) species recorded on more than ten occasions but only rarely in recent years; (iii) species not previously recorded at the quoted time of year e.g. summer visitors not previously recorded so late in the year; (iv) species not previously recorded in such large numbers.

BLACK-THROATED DIVER
One at Llandegfedd Reservoir on 10th October — fourth county record.

RED-THROATED DIVER
One at Pen-y-fan Pond on 4th and 6th April — second county record.

BLACK-NECKED GREBE
A pair in full breeding plumage at Llandegfedd Reservoir on 13th May — first record for this month.

FULMAR
One found dead at Undy on 6th November — third county record.

CORMORANT
A bird showing the white head and neck, characteristic of the Continental race *P.c.sinensis*, at Llandegfedd Reservoir 24th February – 20th March — first county record.

GOOSANDER
Bred successfully for the second consecutive year.

SMEW
One at Llandegfedd Reservoir on 1st February — 6th county record.

BRENT GOOSE
Two on the foreshore at Undy 27th – 29th December and another flying down-channel on 29th October — sixth and seventh county records.

MARSH HARRIER

Two at Penhow on 9th May — fifth county record.

PEREGRINE

Records of over 25 sightings received — a considerable increase over previous years.

CORNCRAKE

One near Abergavenny on 16th July — the first sight-record during the breeding season since 1965.

DOWITCHER

One at Undy on 29th August — second county record.

PECTORAL SANDPIPER

One on saltmarsh at Peterstone Wentlooge on 3rd April — second county record.

AVOCET

Single birds at Uskmouth on 15th May and at Peterstone Wentlooge on 27th August — seventh and eighth county records.

LITTLE TERN

Two at Peterstone Wentlooge on 22nd August and another on 4th September — ninth and tenth county records.

SNOWY OWL

One in the vicinity of Abergavenny during late January — third county record. (At the time of writing, this record is being considered by the British Rarities Committee).

SHORT-EARED OWL

Two at Peterstone Wentlooge on 11th August — 1st record for this month.

SWIFT

One at Rogerstone on 23rd October — latest ever recorded.

RING OUZEL

Two at Mynydd Garn-clochdy on 27th October and two at Peterstone Wentlooge on 31st October — by far the latest ever recorded (none previously in October).

WHEATEAR

One at Peterstone on 16th May was considered to show the characteristics of the Greenland race *O.o.leucorrhoa* — fourth county record.

REDSTART

One at Peterstone Wentlooge on 31st October — latest ever recorded.

BLACKCAP

A large increase in winter records, with at least 16 different birds reported from widely scattered localities between 20th November and the end of the year.

HAWFINCH

Ten at St. Dial's Wood, Monmouth on 29th February — by far the largest party recorded in recent years.

A list of Welsh bird names

The following list of birds includes only those species which are mentioned in this book. The ornithologist wishing to look up and use the Welsh name for many species has in the past encountered problems. Due possibly to the isolating effect of the mountainous terrain, different districts have adopted their own bird names so that for well-known and widely-distributed species there may be up to about a dozen names to choose from. The question of which one should be used is not easily answered. This confusion and uncertainty has at last been remedied by P. Hope Jones and E. Breeze Jones in their List of Welsh Birds published in 1973 by the National Museum of Wales. They have, after much discussion with ornithologists and language experts, selected the most appropriate Welsh name for each species of bird to have occurred within the Principality.

This authoritative list of Welsh Bird Names, together with this introduction was first published in " A Guide to the Birds of Wales " by David Saunders, in 1974, and we are very grateful to him, to the authors, and the National Museum of Wales for allowing us to reproduce this selection of names as an appendix to our book.

The comprehensive list can be obtained from the Zoology Department, National Museum of Wales, Cardiff.

1	Black-throated Diver	Trochydd Gyddfddu
2	Great Northern Diver	Trochydd Mawr
4	Red-throated Diver	Trochydd Gyddfgoch
5	Great Crested Grebe	Gwyach Fawr Gopog
7	Slavonian Grebe	Gwyach Gorniog
8	Black-necked Grebe	Gwyach Yddfddu
9	Little Grebe	Gwyach Fach
12	Leach's Petrel	Pedryn Gynffon-fforchog
14	British Storm Petrel	Pedryn Drycin Prydeinig
16	Manx Shearwater	Aderyn-Drycin Manaw
26	Fulmar	Aderyn-Drycin y Graig
27	Gannet	Hugan
28	Cormorant	Mulfran
29	Shag	Mulfran Werdd
30	Grey Heron	Crëyr Glas
37	Little Bittern	Aderyn-bwn Lleiaf
38	Bittern	Aderyn y Bwn
42	Spoonbill	Llwybig
43	Glossy Ibis	Crymanbig Ddu
45	Mallard	Hwyaden Wyllt
46	Teal	Corhwyaden

47	Garganey	Hwyaden Addfain
49	Gadwall	Hwyaden Lwyd
50	Wigeon	Chwiwell
52	Pintail	Hwyaden Lostfain
53	Shoveler	Hwyaden Lydanbig
54	Red-crested Pochard	Hwyaden Gribgoch
55	Scaup	Hwyaden Benddu
56	Tufted Duck	Hwyaden Gopog
57	Pochard	Hwyaden Bengoch
58	Ferruginous Duck	Hwyaden Lygadwen
60	Goldeneye	Hwyaden Lygad-aur
61	Long-tailed Duck	Hwyaden Gynffon-hir
62	Velvet Scoter	Môr-hwyaden y Gogledd
64	Common Scoter	Môr-hwyaden Ddu
67	Eider	Hwyaden Fwythblu
69	Red-breasted Merganser	Hwyaden Frongoch
70	Goosander	Hwyaden Ddanheddog
71	Smew	Lleian Wen
73	Shelduck	Hwyaden yr Eithin
74	Ruddy Shelduck	Hwyaden Goch yr Eithin
75	Greylag Goose	Gŵydd Wyllt
76	White-fronted Goose	Gŵydd Dalcen-wen
78	Bean Goose	Gŵydd y Llafur
78	Pink-footed Goose	Gŵydd Droedbinc
80	Brent Goose	Gŵydd Ddu
81	Barnacle Goose	Gŵydd Wyran
82	Canada Goose	Gŵydd Canada
84	Mute Swan	Alarch Dof
85	Whooper Swan	Alarch y Gogledd
86	Bewick's Swan	Alarch Bewick
91	Buzzard	Bwncath
92	Rough-legged Buzzard	Bod Bacsiog
93	Sparrowhawk	Gwalch Glas
94	Goshawk	Gwalch Marth
95	Red Kite	Barcud
97	White-tailed Eagle	Eryr y Môr
98	Honey Buzzard	Bod y Mêl
99	Marsh Harrier	Bod y Gwerni
100	Hen Harrier	Bod Tinwen
102	Montagu's Harrier	Bod Montagu
103	Osprey	Gwalch y Pysgod
104	Hobby	Hebog yr Ehedydd
105	Peregrine	Hebog Tramor
107	Merlin	Cudyll Bach
110	Kestrel	Cudyll Coch
111	Red Grouse	Grugiar
113	Black Grouse	Grugiar Ddu
115	Red-legged Partridge	Petrisen Goesgoch

116	Partridge	Petrisen
117	Quail	Sofliar
118	Pheasant	Ffesant
120	Water Rail	Rhegen y Dŵr
121	Spotted Crake	Rhegen Fraith
125	Corncrake	Rhegen yr Ŷd
126	Moorhen	Iâr Ddŵr
127	Coot	Cwtiar
131	Oystercatcher	Pioden y Môr
133	Lapwing	Cornchwiglen
134	Ringed Plover	Cwtiad Torchog
135	Little Ringed Plover	Cwtiad Torchog Bach
139	Grey Plover	Cwtiad Llwyd
140	Golden Plover	Cwtiad Aur
142	Dotterel	Hutan y Mynydd
143	Turnstone	Cwtiad y Traeth
144	Long-billed Dowitcher	Gïach Gylfin-hir
145	Snipe	Gïach Gyffredin
146	Great Snipe	Gïach Fawr
147	Jack Snipe	Gïach Fach
148	Woodcock	Cyffylog
150	Curlew	Gylfinir
151	Whimbrel	Coegylfinir
154	Black-tailed Godwit	Rhostog Gynffonddu
155	Bar-tailed Godwit	Rhostog Gynffonfrith
156	Green Sandpiper	Pibydd Gwyrdd
157	Wood Sandpiper	Pibydd y Graean
159	Common Sandpiper	Pibydd y Dorlan
161	Redshank	Pibydd Coesgoch
162	Spotted Redshank	Pibydd Coesgoch Mannog
165	Greenshank	Pibydd Coeswerdd
169	Knot	Pibydd yr Aber
170	Purple Sandpiper	Pibydd Du
171	Little Stint	Pibydd Bach
176	Pectoral Sandpiper	Pibydd Cain
178	Dunlin	Pibydd y Mawn
179	Curlew Sandpiper	Pibydd Cambig
181	Sanderling	Pibydd y Tywod
184	Ruff	Pibydd Torchog
185	Avocet	Cambig
187	Grey Phalarope	Llydandroed Llwyd
188	Red-necked Phalarope	Llydandroed Gyddfgoch
189	Stone Curlew	Rhedwr y Moelydd
193	Arctic Skua	Sgiwen y Gogledd
194	Great Skua	Sgiwen Fawr
196	Long-tailed Skua	Sgiwen Lostfain
198	Great Black-backed Gull	Gwylan Gefnddu Fwyaf
199	Lesser Black-backed Gull	Gwylan Gefnddu Leiaf

143

200	Herring Gull	Gwylan y Penwaig
201	Common Gull	Gwylan y Gweunydd
202	Glaucous Gull	Gwylan y Gogledd
205	Mediterranean Gull	Gwylan Môr y Canoldir
207	Little Gull	Gwylan Fechan
208	Black-headed Gull	Gwylan Benddu
211	Kittiwake	Gwylan Goesddu
212	Black Tern	Corswennol Ddu
217	Common Tern	Morwennol Gyffredin
218	Arctic Tern	Morwennol y Gogledd
222	Little Tern	Morwennol Fechan
223	Sandwich Tern	Morwennol Bigddu
224	Razorbill	Llurs
226	Little Auk	Carfil Bach
227	Guillemot	Gwylog
230	Puffin	Pâl
232	Stock Dove	Colomen Wyllt
234	Woodpigeon	Ysguthan
235	Turtle Dove	Turtur
	Collared Dove	Turtur Dorchog
237	Cuckoo	Cog
241	Barn Owl	Tylluan Wen
244	Snowy Owl	Tylluan yr Eira
246	Little Owl	Tylluan Fach
247	Tawny Owl	Tylluan Frech
248	Long-eared Owl	Tylluan Gorniog
249	Short-eared Owl	Tylluan Glustiog
252	Nightjar	Troellwr Mawr
255	Swift	Gwennol Ddu
258	Kingfisher	Glas y Dorlan
261	Hoopoe	Copog
262	Green Woodpecker	Cnocell Werdd
263	Great Spotted Woodpecker	Cnocell Fraith Fwyaf
264	Lesser Spotted Woodpecker	Cnocell Fraith Leiaf
265	Wryneck	Pengam
271	Woodlark	Ehedydd y Coed
272	Skylark	Ehedydd
273	Shore Lark	Ehedydd y Traeth
274	Swallow	Gwennol
276	House Martin	Gwennol y Bondo
277	Sand Martin	Gwennol y Glennydd
278	Golden Oriole	Euryn
279	Raven	Cigfran
280	Carrion Crow	Brân Dyddyn
282	Rook	Ydfran
283	Jackdaw	Jac-y-do
284	Magpie	Pioden
285	Nutcracker	Malwr Cnau

286	Jay	Ysgrech y Coed
287	Chough	Brân Goesgoch
288	Great Tit	Titw Mawr
289	Blue Tit	Titw Tomos Las
290	Coal Tit	Titw Penddu
292	Marsh Tit	Titw'r Wern
293	Willow Tit	Titw'r Helyg
294	Long-tailed Tit	Titw Gynffon-hir
295	Bearded Tit	Titw Barfog
296	Nuthatch	Delor y Cnau
298	Treecreeper	Dringwr Bach
299	Wren	Dryw
300	Dipper	Bronwen y Dŵr
301	Mistle Thrush	Brych y Coed
302	Fieldfare	Socan Eira
303	Song Thrush	Bronfraith
304	Redwing	Coch dan-aden
307	Ring Ouzel	Mwyalchen y Mynydd
308	Blackbird	Mwyalchen
311	Wheatear	Tinwen y Garn
317	Stonechat	Clochdar y Cerrig
318	Whinchat	Crec yr Eithin
320	Redstart	Tingoch
321	Black Redstart	Tingoch Du
322	Nightingale	Eos
325	Robin	Robin Goch
327	Grasshopper Warbler	Troellwr Bach
333	Reed Warbler	Telor y Cyrs
334	Marsh Warbler	Telor y Gwerni
337	Sedge Warbler	Telor yr Hesg
338	Aquatic Warbler	Telor y Dŵr
339	Melodious Warbler	Telor Pêr
340	Icterine Warbler	Telor Aur
341	Olivaceous Warbler	Telor Llwyd
343	Blackcap	Telor Penddu
346	Garden Warbler	Telor yr Ardd
347	Whitethroat	Llwydfron
348	Lesser Whitethroat	Llwydfron Fach
354	Willow Warbler	Telor yr Helyg
356	Chiffchaff	Siff-saff
357	Wood Warbler	Telor y Coed
364	Goldcrest	Dryw Eurben
365	Firecrest	Dryw Penfflamgoch
366	Spotted Flycatcher	Gwybedog Mannog
368	Pied Flycatcher	Gwybedog Brith
370	Red-breasted Flycatcher	Gwybedog Brongoch
371	Dunnock	Llwyd y Gwrych
373	Meadow Pipit	Corhedydd y Waun

374	Richard's Pipit	Corhedydd Richard
376	Tree Pipit	Corhedydd y Coed
379	Rock Pipit	Corhedydd y Graig
380	Pied Wagtail	Siglen Fraith
381	Grey Wagtail	Siglen Lwyd
382	Yellow Wagtail	Siglen Felen
382	Blue-headed Wagtail	Siglen Benlas
383	Waxwing	Cynffon Sidan
384	Great Grey Shrike	Cigydd Mawr
386	Woodchat Shrike	Cigydd Bengoch
388	Red-backed Shrike	Cigydd Cefngoch
389	Starling	Drudwen
390	Rose-coloured Starling	Drudwen Wridog
391	Hawfinch	Gylfinbraff
392	Greenfinch	Llinos Werdd
393	Goldfinch	Nico
394	Siskin	Pila Gwyrdd
395	Linnet	Llinos
396	Twite	Llinos y Mynydd
397	Redpoll	Llinos Bengoch
401	Bullfinch	Coch y Berllan
404	Crossbill	Gylfin Groes
406	Two-barred Crossbill	Croesbig Wenaden
407	Chaffinch	Ji-binc
408	Brambling	Pinc y Mynydd
409	Yellowhammer	Bras Melyn
410	Corn Bunting	Bras yr Ŷd
415	Cirl Bunting	Bras Ffrainc
416	Ortolan Bunting	Bras y Gerddi
421	Reed Bunting	Bras y Cyrs
422	Lapland Bunting	Bras y Gogledd
423	Snow Bunting	Bras yr Eira
424	House Sparrow	Aderyn y To
425	Tree Sparrow	Golfan y Mynydd

APPENDIX 2   Place names and map references

The three lists below are intended to assist the reader to locate the sites mentioned in the text, for some of which the locations might not be found without considerable map searching. The four-figure reference given for each site represents the one-kilometre square in which either the site lies completely or from which it can be readily identified; for some of the larger sites which extend over several squares the choice of reference is thus somewhat arbitrary.

The first list gives references for all the B.T.O. registered sites in the county, even though in some cases their names would reveal their location adequately. The second gives references for other places in Gwent mentioned in the text; the third gives those that are outside Gwent.

LIST 1.   B.T.O. REGISTERED SITES

Abergavenny sewage works	SO 2913	Over Monnow	SO 5012
Blorenge	SO 2611	Pant-gwyn Pools	ST 2594
Caldicot Moor	ST 4586	Pant-yr-eos Reservoir	ST 2591
Cwmcarn	ST 2393	Park Wood	ST 2486
Cwm Clydach	SO 2112	Part-y-seal Wood	SO 4224
Cwm Tyleri	SO 2207	Pen-y-fan Pond	SO 1900
Cwmyoy	SO 3023	Peterstone Pill	ST 2780
Denny Island	ST 4581	Piercefield Wood	ST 5395
Garnlydan Reservoir	SO 1712	Ponthir	ST 3393
Goldcliff Point	ST 3781	Reddings Inclosure	SO 5313
Golden Hill Wood	ST 4297	Rookery Wood, Pant-y-Goitre	SO 3408
King's Wood	SO 4712	Skirrid Fawr	SO 3217
Lasgarn Wood	SO 2704	St. Pierre Lake	ST 5190
Llanarth Court	SO 3810	Sugar Loaf	SO 2718
Llandegfedd Reservoir	ST 3299	Tintern	SO 5200
Llanvihangel Gobion	SO 3409	Trefil Quarries	SO 1213
Llanwenarth	SO 2714	Twmbarlwm	ST 2492
Magor Reserve	ST 4286	Undy foreshore	ST 4485
Miers Bog	SO 2814	Uskmouth	ST 3282
Minnetts Wood	ST 4489	Wentwood	ST 4093
Mon.–Brecon Canal,		Wern Farm	SO 3001
Rogerstone	ST 2689	Whitson	ST 3783
Nedern Meadow	ST 4889	Wyndcliff	ST 5297
Newport Docks	ST 3185	Ynysyfro Reservoir	ST 2889
Olway Meadow	SO 4102		

LIST 2.   OTHER SITES WITHIN GWENT

Abercarn	ST 2195	Carno Reservoir	SO 1613
Bassaleg	ST 2786	Cefntilla Court	SO 4002
Beaufort	SO 1611	Cleddon Wood	ST 5103
Bedwin Sands	ST 4783	Coed Morgan	SO 3511
Bertholey	ST 3994	Collister Pill	ST 4585
Bettws Newydd	SO 3505	Crick	ST 4890
Bishton	ST 3887	Croesyceiliog	ST 3096
Black Rock (coastal)	ST 5188	Cross Ash	SO 4019
Blackrock (inland)	SO 2112	Crumlin	ST 2198
The Bryn	SO 3309	Cwmavon	SO 2606
Brynmawr	SO 1911	Devauden	ST 4898
Bulmore	ST 3591	Dewstow	ST 4688
Caerleon	ST 3390	Dingestow	SO 4512
Caerwent	ST 4790	Dinham	ST 4790

Fforest Coal Pit	SO 2820	Manmoel	SO 1803
Garndiffaith	SO 2604	Mardy	SO 3015
Glascoed	SO 3301	Marshfield	ST 2682
Govilon	SO 2613	Monkswood	SO 3402
Goytre	SO 3206	Nantyderry	SO 3405
Grwyne Fawr	SO 2822	Newbridge-on-Usk	ST 3894
Hafodyrynys	ST 2399	Oakdale	ST 1898
Kemeys Inferior	ST 3892	Pandy	SO 3322
Kilgwrrwg	ST 4798	Parc Seymour	ST 4091
Livox Quarries	ST 5497	Penhow	ST 4290
Llanbadoc	SO 3700	Penpergwm	SO 3210
Llandenny	SO 4103	Pontllanfraith	ST 1796
Llandowlais	ST 3798	Pontnewydd	ST 2996
Llanellen	SO 3010	Portskewett	ST 5088
Llanfoist	SO 2813	Pwlldu	SO 2411
Llangwm	SO 4200	Redwick	ST 4184
Llangybi	ST 3796	Rhymney	SO 1107
Llanhilleth	SO 2100	Rogiet	ST 4687
Llanover	SO 3108	St. Brides Wentlooge	ST 2982
Llantarnam	ST 3093	St. Dials Wood (Monmouth)	SO 5011
Llanthony	SO 2827	Severn Tunnel Junction	ST 4687
Llantrisant	ST 3996	Shirenewton	ST 4893
Llanvair Discoed	ST 4492	Skenfrith	SO 4520
Llanvapley	SO 3614	Sluice Farm (Peterstone)	ST 2579
Llanvihangel-Ystern-Llewern	SO 4313	Sor Brook	ST 3494
Llanwern	ST 3688	Sudbrook	ST 5087
Llwyndu	SO 2816	Trelleck	SO 5005
Lydart	SO 5009	Treworgan Common	SO 4205
Maesglas	ST 2985	Trostrey	SO 3804
Maesycwmmer	ST 1594	Twyn Ceilog	SO 1012
Magor Pill	ST 4384	Uskmouth ash ponds	ST 3382
Malpas	ST 3090	Upper Cwmbran	ST 2796
Mamhilad	SO 3003		

LIST 3. SITES OUTSIDE GWENT

Brean Down	Som.	ST 2859	Rumney Flats	S. Glam.	ST 2377
Flat Holm	S. Glam.	ST 2264	Sand Point	Avon	ST 3165
Gilfach Goch	Mid. Glam.	SS 9889	Steart Island	Som.	ST 2948
Lavernock Point	S. Glam.	ST 1868	Steep Holm	Som.	ST 2260
Llangattock cliffs	Powys	SO 1915	Talybont		
Llangorse Lake	Powys	SO 1326	Reservoir	Powys	SO 0918
Roath Park,			Whiteford Point	W. Glam.	SS 4496
Cardiff	S. Glam.	ST 1879			

APPENDIX 3   Some Useful Addresses

Gwent Ornithological Society
Mr. H. W. Hamar, ' Andorra,' Sunlea Crescent, Pontypool, Gwent.

Gwent Trust for Nature Conservation
Commander G. G. Cowburn, The Cwm, Llantrissent, Nr. Usk.

British Trust for Ornithology (Gwent Representative)
Mr. P. N. Martin, 16 Royal Oak Close, Machen, Newport.

Brecknock County Naturalists' Trust
Mr. E. Bartlett, Chapel House, Llechfaen, Brecon, Powys.

Bristol Ornithological Club
Mrs. J. Copeland, Rock House, 19 St. George's Hill,
    Easton-in-Gordano, Bristol BS20 0PS.

Cardiff Naturalists' Society, Ornithological Section
Mr. C. G. Trew, 26 Parc Castell-y-Mynach, Creigiau, Nr. Cardiff, S. Glam.

Gloucester Naturalists' Society
Mr. C. M. Swaine, Mill House, Rendcombe, Cirencester, Gloucestershire.

Herefordshire Ornithological Club
Mrs. J. M. Bromley, The Garth, Kington, Herefordshire.

Somerset Ornithological Society
Mr. A. J. Parsons, ' Bamfield,' Tower Hill Road, Crewkerne, Somerset.

Royal Society for the Protection of Birds (Welsh Office)
Mr. R. Lovegrove, 18 High Street, Newtown, Powys.

REFERENCES

BANNERMAN, D. A. 1953. *The Birds of the British Isles.* Vol. II. Oliver and Boyd, Edinburgh.

BATTEN, L. A. 1973. Bird population changes for the years 1971–72. Bird Study, 20: 303–307.

BATTEN, L. A., and MARCHANT, J. H. 1975a. Bird population changes for the years 1972–73. Bird Study, 22: 99–104.

BATTEN, L. A. and MARCHANT, J. H. 1975b. Swallows take a dive. B.T.O. News, 75: 2–3.

BATTEN, L. A. and MARCHANT, J. H. 1976. Bird population changes for the years 1973–74. Bird Study, 23: 11–20.

BOYD, H. J. 1963. The Denny. In, Steep Holm Gull Research Station Report, 1963: 28. Mimeograph.

THE BRITISH ORNITHOLOGISTS' UNION. 1971. *The Status of Birds in Britain and Ireland.* Blackwell, Oxford.

CHADWICK, P. J. 1962. Reports from bird observatories. Steep Holm, Somerset. Bird Migration, 2: 127–128.

CHAPMAN, L. B. 1955. Studies of a Tree Swallow colony. Bird-Banding, 26: 45–70.

CLAFTON, F. R. 1976. Portland Bill. In, *Bird Observatories in Britain and Ireland.* Ed. R. Durman, 191–205. T. & A. D. Poyser, Berkhamstead.

DAVIS, A. H. 1971. Past status of sea-birds in the Bristol Channel. Bristol Ornithology, 4: 147–158.

Davis, P. E. and HOPE JONES, P. 1970. Welsh Bird Report 1969. Nature Wales, 12: 112–128.

EASTWOOD, E. 1967. *Radar Ornithology.* Methuen, London.

Evans, P. R. and SMITH, P. C. 1975. Studies of shorebirds at Lindisfarne, Northumberland. 2. Fat and pectoral muscle as indicators of body condition in the Bar-tailed Godwit. Wildfowl, 26: 64–76.

FERNS, P. N. 1975. Development proposals for the Severn Estuary and the status of Gwent waders. Gwent Bird Report, 1 (10): 495–501.

FLEGG, J. J. M. and GLUE, D. E. 1971. *Nestboxes.* B.T.O. Field Guide No. 3 (4th ed.), Tring.

GREEN, G. H. 1976. Celtic Wader Research Group, Report No. 1. Mimeograph.

HAMAR, H. W. and WILKINSON, K. 1969. Coastal migration watch at Goldcliff on 6th and 19th October. Monmouthshire Birds, 1 (4): 125–126.

HANSFORD, P. R. 1976. Population dynamics of wintering thrushes. B.Sc. Thesis, University College, Cardiff.

HARRIS, M. P. 1972. Inter-island movements of Manx Shearwaters. Bird Study, 19: 167–171.

HEATHCOTE, A., GRIFFIN, D. and SALMON, H. M. 1967. *The Birds of Glamorgan.* Cardiff Naturalists' Society, Cardiff.

HOLT, E. G. 1950. Autumn migration along the Bristol Channel. Br. Birds, 43: 271–273.

HOLT, E. G. 1960. Visible autumn migration along the Bristol Channel. Report on Somerset Birds, 46: 58–64.

HOOKER, A. V. 1970. Severnside of the future. Proc. Instn. Civ. Engrs., 47: 337–348.

HOPE JONES, P. and DAVIS, P. E. 1973. Welsh Bird Report for 1972. Nature Wales, 13: 239–251.

Hope Jones, P. and Davis, P. E. 1975.   Welsh Bird Report for 1973. Nature Wales, 14: 256–269.

Humphreys, P. N. 1963.   *The Birds of Monmouthshire*. Newport Museum, Newport.

Humphreys, P. N. 1975.   House Martins as a hobby. Gwent Bird Report, 1 (10): 505–507.

Ingram, G. C. S. and Salmon, H. M. 1939.   The Birds of Monmouthshire. Trans. Cardiff Nat. Soc., 60: 93–127.

Jones, W. E. 1966.   Sea-watching in Glamorgan. Seabird Group Bulletin, 2: 18–20.

King, B. and Perrett, D. H. 1963.   A marked movement of Kittiwakes on the Somerset coast. Report on Somerset Birds, 49: 57–59.

Lack, D. 1963.   Migration across the southern North Sea studied by radar. Part 5. Movements in August, winter and spring, and conclusions. Ibis, 105: 461–492.

Lack, D. and Lack, E. 1949.   Passerine migration through England. Br. Birds, 42: 320–326.

Lewis, W. G. 1968.   Introduction. Monmouthshire Birds, 1(3): 67–70.

Lloyd, A. J. 1942.   Studies on the biology of the Bristol Channel. IX. A survey of the fishing industry at Weston-super-Mare during the winter of 1940–41. Proc. Bristol Nat. Soc., 9: 316–327.

Lockley, R. M. 1953.   On the movements of the Manx Shearwater at sea during the breeding season. Br. Birds, Supplementary Number, 46: 1–48.

Matheson, C. 1932.   *Changes in the Fauna of Wales during Historic Times*. National Museum of Wales, Cardiff.

Mackie, P. 1976.   A short note on Redshank in the upper Clyde Estuary. Wader Study Group Bulletin, 17: 5–10.

Mayer-Gross, H. 1970.   *Nest Record Scheme*. B.T.O. Field Guide No. 12, Tring.

Mead, C. J. 1974.   *Bird Ringing*. B.T.O. Field Guide No. 16, Tring.

Minton, C. D. T. 1973.   Seasonal variations in the weights of waders on the Wash. Wash Wader Ringing Group Report 1971/2, Appendix 4. Mimeograph.

Minton, C. D. T. 1975.   The waders of the Wash — ringing and biometric studies. Mimeographed Report (Wash Feasibility Study).

Morley, J. V. 1972.   Migration routes in the vicinity of Bridgwater Bay, Somerset. Bristol Ornithology, 5: 191–194.

Parslow, J. L. F. 1973.   *Breeding Birds of Britain and Ireland: a Historical Survey* T. and A. D. Poyser, Berkhamsted.

Penhallurick, R. D. 1969.   *Birds of the Cornish Coast*. D. B. Barton, Truro.

Perrins, C. M., Harris, M. P. and Britton, C. K. 1973.   Survival of Manx Shearwaters *Puffinus puffinus*. Ibis, 115: 535–548.

Playford, P. F. J. 1972.   The early bird catches the — cold. Monmouthshire Birds, 1 (7): 304–306.

Playford, P. F. J. 1976.   Nestbox colonies. Gwent Bird Report, 11: 16–22.

Prater, A. J. 1974.   *Birds of Estuaries Enquiry 1971–72*. B.T.O./R.S.P.B./W.T., Tring.

Prater, A. J. 1975a.   Fat and weight changes of waders in winter. Ringing and Migration, 1: 43–47.

Prater, A. J. 1975b.   *Birds of Estuaries Enquiry 1972–73*. B.T.O./R.S.P.B./W.T., Tring.

Prater, A. J. 1976.   *Birds of Estuaries Enquiry 1973–74*. B.T.O./R.S.P.B./W.T., Tring.

Rabbitts, B. 1971.   Bristol Channel sea-bird survey — present status of species. Bristol Ornithology, 4: 159–171.

RABBITTS, B. 1972. Recent changes in the status of the Kittiwake off the Somerset coast. Bristol Ornithology, 5: 201–204.

RAINES, R. J. H. 1950. Observations on passage migration in the Trent valley and inland migration. Br. Birds, 43: 97–112.

ROGERS, A. E. F. 1970. Local movements of Sand Martins on the river Usk. Nature Wales, 12: 7–9.

ROGERS, A. E. F. and GAULT, L. N. 1968. The distribution of Sand Martins on the river Usk. Nature Wales, 11: 15–19.

SAINSBURY, M. 1972. Visible migration along the south-east shores of the Severn estuary. Bristol Ornithology, 5: 195–200.

SALMON, H. M. 1974. *A Supplement to the Birds of Glamorgan 1967.* Cardiff Naturalists' Society, Cardiff.

SARSON, E. T. 1969. Notes on the effect of abnormal summer rainfall on the Sand Martin colonies on the river Usk. Monmouthshire Birds, 1(4): 120–121.

SHARROCK, J. T. R. 1976. *The Atlas of Breeding Birds in Britain and Ireland.* B.T.O./ I.W.C., Tring.

SHAW, T. L. 1974. Tidal energy from the Severn estuary. Nature, Lond., 249: 730-733.

SPENCER, R. and HUDSON, R. 1976. Report on bird-ringing for 1974. Bird Study, 23: Special supplement, 1–64.

VENABLES, W. A. 1974. The year at Peterstone Pill. Gwent Bird Report, 1(9): 426–430.

WINSTANLEY, D., SPENCER, R. and WILLIAMSON, K. 1974. Where have all the White-throats gone? Bird Study, 21: 1–14.

Gwent

POWYS

Afon Honddu

A 40 (T)

A 465 (T)

B 4248

A 467

A 4043

TREDEGAR

EBBW VALE

ABERTILLERY

R Sirhowy

A 4046

PONTYPOOL

A 472

MID GLAMORGAN

A 4048

CWMBRAN

A 472

A 4048

RISCA

R Ebbw

SOUTH GLAMORGAN

A 48 (T)

MILES
0 1 2 3 4 5

0 1 2 3 4 5 6 7 8
KILOMETRES